Really learn

100 more

phrasal verbs

OXFORD

UNIVERSITY PRESS

OXFORD
UNIVERSITY PRESS

Great Clarendon Street, Oxford OX2 6DP

Oxford University Press is a department of the University of Oxford.
It furthers the University's objective of excellence in research, scholarship,
and education by publishing worldwide in

Oxford New York

Auckland Cape Town Dar es Salaam Hong Kong Karachi
Kuala Lumpur Madrid Melbourne Mexico City Nairobi
New Delhi Shanghai Taipei Toronto

With offices in

Argentina Austria Brazil Chile Czech Republic France Greece
Guatemala Hungary Italy Japan Poland Portugal Singapore
South Korea Switzerland Thailand Turkey Ukraine Vietnam

OXFORD and OXFORD ENGLISH are registered trade marks of
Oxford University Press in the UK and in certain other countries

The British National Corpus is a collaborative project involving Oxford
University Press, Longman, Chambers, the Universities of Oxford and
Lancaster and the British Library

ISBN-13: 978 0 19 431745 0

Edited by Dilys Parkinson
Assisted by Jennifer Bradbery

Printed in China

Contents

How to Really Learn More Phrasal Verbs

This book covers a further 100 of the most frequent and useful phrasal verbs in English. Each verb is presented on a single page, with examples and exercises that are designed to show the meaning and the situations in which it is most commonly used. Although some of the verbs may have other meanings, only the most important meanings for everyday English have been included.

Each page can be studied on its own, so you can look at the verbs in any order, but the exercises on each page should be worked through in the order they are written.

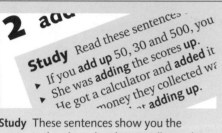

Study These sentences show you the contexts the phrasal verb is usually used in and all the possible grammar patterns.

Check Use the examples in the Study box to check that you understand the meaning of the verb and the grammar patterns. You should check your answers in the key at the back of the book before you move on to the Practise section.

Practise These exercises enable you to practise using the verb in a natural way. If you have difficulty, look back at the Study and Check sections. After completing the exercises, you should check your answers carefully in the key.

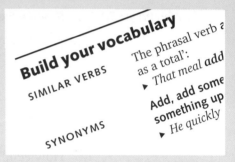

Build your vocabulary gives extra information about the phrasal verb such as related nouns or adjectives, synonyms (single words and other phrasal verbs) and opposites, other meanings of the verb, or verbs with similar or related meanings. This will help you to increase your vocabulary and understand more phrasal verbs.

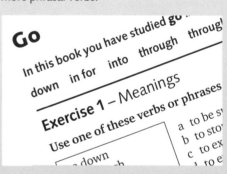

In the centre of the book are some pages for **revision and review**. They look, for example, at the meanings of the particles used with phrasal verbs or group verbs into themes. The exercises will help you review what you have learned and give you practice for exams. There is a key at the end of the section.

Tips for learning phrasal verbs

How else can you learn phrasal verbs? Here are some ideas:

Keeping records

It is helpful to keep paper or electronic vocabulary records for phrasal verbs:

- Write down and learn verbs as vocabulary units (as if they are single words) as you meet them.
- Make a note of whether they have an object or not e.g. *be over, count on sb/sth, let sb off* (see also p. iv). Can the verb be used in the passive?
- Note some common subjects and objects the verb is used with and the grammar patterns.
- It may help you to remember the meaning and grammar if you write down a couple of examples. You could even add your own cartoons.
- You can keep a note of opposites too or a single-word verb with the same meaning.
- Add any related nouns and adjectives that you find.

verb:	mess sth up; mess up
meaning:	to spoil or ruin sth/sb, to do sth badly
objects:	life, arrangements, people, job
grammar:	mess sth up, mess up sth mess it up, mess up, get messed up
synonym:	foul sth up

verb:	let sb off, let sb off sth
meaning:	to allow sb not to do or pay sth
example:	I'll let you off this time.

Grouping verbs

Here are some different ways of grouping the verbs in your records to help you remember them:

- according to their particles (*up, down, out*, etc.) and particular meanings of the particles (e.g. for **up**: increasing – *brush sth up*; finishing – *eat sth up*) (See Review page 8). Add new phrasal verbs as you meet them.
- Some verbs, like **go** and **take** form many phrasal verbs with different particles (see Review pages 2 and 3). You can group phrasal verbs under the main verb in your records.
- You can group them by themes (at home, at work, travelling, telephoning, etc.).
- When you are revising or reviewing phrasal verbs, try to group them in a different way. You may like to try writing a short story. For example, you could write about your day at work and use the verbs: *fit sb/sth in, get around to sth, look into sth, mess sth up, see to sth, throw sth out*, etc.

Meeting new phrasal verbs

- When you meet a verb you don't know, try to guess its meaning first, using the context and what you know about the meaning of particles. This will also help you with phrasal verbs that are very new to the language as they are often formed with a word and a particle with a common meaning, for example **head up**.

The position of objects in phrasal verbs

Some phrasal verbs in this book do not have objects: for example *add up* (1), *be over*.

The majority of phrasal verbs in the book do have an object. The exercises on each verb will help you to find out and remember where to put the object, but here are some simple guidelines to help you:

1 Verb + preposition

These are verbs such as *consist of*, *do without*, *refer to* and *run into*. *Do away with*, *grow out of* and other verbs with 3 parts are also in this group. As you will see, the object can only come **after** the last part of the verb (a preposition), whether it is a noun or a pronoun:

▶ *Each team **consists of** 15 players.*
▶ *I **ran into** an old friend yesterday.*
▶ *I **ran into** her yesterday.*
▶ *Jack has **grown out of** all his clothes!*

2 Verb + adverb

In other verbs, such as *brush up*, *pass on*, *point out* and *try on*, the second part of the verb is an adverb. In these cases, the noun can be placed either **after** the adverb or **between** the verb and the adverb. A pronoun must always come **between** the verb and the adverb:

▶ *I'd like to **try on** this jacket.*
▶ *I'd like to **try** this jacket **on**.*
▶ *I'd like to **try** it **on**.*

If the object is a long phrase, it usually comes **after** the verb:

▶ *He **pointed out** the room I had to go to for my interview.*

The examples and exercises will show you which patterns to use for a particular verb. The key will also tell you if one pattern is more common for a verb than others. You may find it useful to note the patterns in your vocabulary records.

Other reference material

- *Really Learn 100 Phrasal Verbs* will add another 100 verbs to your vocabulary, with their related words, synonyms, opposites and other similar verbs. You will then be well equipped to use phrasal verbs naturally in your speaking and writing and to cope with them in exams.
- *Really Learn 100 Phrasal Verbs for Business* will help you learn phrasal verbs that are frequently used in the world of business.
- Use a dictionary to help you learn more verbs. The *Oxford Phrasal Verbs Dictionary for learners* contains more than 7,000 phrasal verbs.

1 add up

- ▸ Why would she take a job with longer hours and less money? It doesn't **add up**.
- ▸ There was something about his story which didn't quite **add up**.
- ▸ It all **adds up** now. I was sure he was hiding something from me.

Check Use the sentences in the Study box to help you do these exercises.

MEANING

Use <u>two</u> of the words below to complete this meaning of *add up*:

reasonable   silly   clever   sensible

If something **adds up**, it seems

_____ or _____

GRAMMAR

Which of these are grammatically possible for this verb?

a His story didn't add up.
b I added up his story.
c His story certainly adds up.
d His story was added up.

→ Now check your answers in the key.

Practise

1 Match the two halves to make complete sentences.

a The government's policy on housing
b I was confused because
c When she said who she was
d I thought about all the facts but

i what she said didn't add up.
ii doesn't add up.
iii they didn't add up.
iv it all started to add up.

2 Complete the sentences with the correct form of *add up*.

a Why didn't he call her? It doesn't _____ .

b It all _____ now. He didn't tell me because he was planning a surprise.

c The things she said just didn't _____ .

d I listened carefully to their story, but nothing _____ .

e I was looking over my notes on the case and there were a few things that

_____ .

f Now I know where she was last night, it's all beginning _____ .

→ Now check your answers in the key.

Build your vocabulary

OTHER MEANINGS **Add up** can also mean 'to increase gradually to a large number or amount':

- ▸ *I save a little money every month — it soon **adds up**.*
- ▸ *None of his jobs had been remarkable, but they all **added up**.*

2 add up; add something up

Study Read these sentences carefully.
- ▶ If you **add up** 50, 30 and 500, you get 580.
- ▶ She was **adding** the scores **up**.
- ▶ He got a calculator and **added** it **up**.
- ▶ All the money they collected was **added up**.
- ▶ I'm really bad at **adding up**.

Check Use the sentences in the Study box to help you do these exercises.

MEANING

If you *add something up*, what do you do?

a you mix two or more things together
b you fix something to something else
c you calculate the total of two or more numbers or amounts

GRAMMAR

Which of these are grammatically possible?

a Can you add up?
b Can you add the numbers up?
c Can you add up it?
d Can you add it up?
e The numbers were added up.

→ Now check your answers in the key.

Practise

1 Choose the correct form of *add up* to fill the gaps in these sentences. You will not need to use them all.

adding them up   adds it up   added up   will add up   was added up

a I _____ the costs, and realized it would be an expensive trip.

b Here's a list of prices. Would you mind _____?

c The score _____ by the referee.

d If you can wait a minute, I _____ how much we've spent.

2 Write a suitable answer to these questions using a form of *add up* or *add something up*.

a How much did the wedding cost in total?

    I don't know, we _____.

b Could we have the bill, please?

    Yes, certainly. I'll _____.

→ Now check your answers in the key.

Build your vocabulary

SIMILAR VERBS   The phrasal verb **add up to...** means 'to have a particular amount as a total':
- ▶ *The numbers **add up to** exactly 100.*
- ▶ *That meal **adds up to** about 600 calories.*

SYNONYMS   **Add, add something** can be used as a synonym of **add up, add something up**, but not of **add up to something**:
- ▶ *He quickly **added** all the numbers.*

3 back somebody or something up

Study Read these sentences carefully.
- You don't have any evidence to **back up** these ridiculous claims!
- I am afraid — and the statistics **back** this **up** — that crime is on the increase.
- I'll say this at the meeting, but only if you're prepared to **back** me **up**.
- Her theories were **backed up** by the results of the experiments.
- You need a business plan **backed up** with lots of market research and hard work.

Check Use the sentences in the Study box to help you do these exercises.

MEANING

Which **one** of these is the correct definition of *back somebody or something up*?
a to know that something is true
b to say or show that what somebody says is true
c to say that you know what somebody says is untrue

GRAMMAR

Which of these are grammatically possible?
a I knew you'd back up me on this.
b Will you back me up on this?
c He wanted me to back up his claims.
d He expects to be backed up.

→ Now check your answers in the key.

Practise

1 Which words can go with *back up*? Choose the right phrase.
a Scientists need to back up *their findings / their students* with evidence.
b The writer's opinions are not backed up by enough *examples / guesses*.
c I'll be quite happy to back up *what you say / what you imagine*.
d The police didn't have enough evidence to back up *the accusations / the crime*, and they had to release him.

2 Rewrite the underlined words using *back somebody or something up* and any other words you need.
a I don't think I believe you. Is there anybody else who can confirm what you're saying?

_____

b It's a shame James isn't here, because he would definitely agree with me about this.

_____

c These ideas may seem outrageous to you, but they are in fact supported by most of the world's scientists nowadays.

_____

→ Now check your answers in the key.

Build your vocabulary

OTHER MEANINGS This verb can also mean 'to help and support somebody':
- *The two doctors **were backed up** by a team of nurses.*

4 be over

Study Read these sentences carefully.

▸ The strike may soon **be over**.
▸ When my training **is over**, I will be a qualified cook.
▸ After the interview **was over**, I took a train home.
▸ The winds and rain are easing now, so the worst **is over**.

Check Use the sentences in the Study box to help you do these exercises.

MEANING

If something *is over*, which of the following is true?

a It has not yet started.
b It is still continuing.
c It has finished.

GRAMMAR

Which of these are grammatically possible?

a The two sides are over the war.
b The war is over.

→ Now check your answers in the key.

Practise

1 Rearrange the words to make complete sentences.

a evening I over didn't to want be the

_____

b comment trial the over wouldn't he until was

_____

c over will troubles soon our be

_____

2 Finish the responses to the following statements in any way you like, using a form of *be over* and any other words you need. You may like to use some of the words below.

nearly   soon   my life   the project   the meeting   my marriage

a I'm fed up with working so hard.
   Don't worry, _____.
b Why did you leave Paris?
   Because _____.
c How did you feel when your husband left you?
   I felt as though _____.
d When will you be coming home?
   When _____.

→ Now check your answers in the key.

Build your vocabulary

OPPOSITES   **be on**
                 This verb is in *Really Learn 100 Phrasal Verbs*.

SIMILAR VERBS   **get over somebody or something**
                 This verb is in *Really Learn 100 Phrasal Verbs*.

5 **blow** something **up**

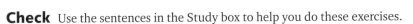

Study Read these sentences carefully.
- We **blew up** lots of balloons for the party.
- They used the pump to **blow** the air bed **up**.
- The balloon will burst if you **blow** it **up** too much.
- Can you check the tyres? I think they need to **be blown up** a bit.

Check Use the sentences in the Study box to help you do these exercises.

MEANING

1 Use two of these words to complete this meaning of *blow something up*:

water   gas   air   petrol   wind

to fill something with _____ or

_____

2 Which of the following can you *blow up*?

a a cushion
b a balloon
c your cheeks
d a tennis ball
e a tyre
f a car

GRAMMAR

Which of these are grammatically possible?

a We blew the balloons up.
b We blew up the balloons.
c We blew them up.
d We blew up them.
e The balloons were blown up.

→ Now check your answers in the key.

Practise

Answer these questions in any way you like, using the verb *blow something up* in each.

a Is everything ready for the party?

 No, _____.

b Did you check the tyres on my bicycle for me?

 _____.

c Where will Jack sleep tonight?

 _____.

→ Now check your answers in the key.

Build your vocabulary

RELATED WORDS   ADJECTIVE: **'blow-up** (This is only used before a noun.)
- *We bought him a **blow-up** pillow for the long bus journey.*

SYNONYMS   To **inflate something** is a more formal verb.

OPPOSITES   To **let something down**:
- *Who has **let** my tyres **down**?*

OTHER MEANINGS   **Blow something up** also means 'to make something larger', for example a photograph, a picture, etc:
- *What a great photo! Shall we have it **blown up**?*

SIMILAR VERBS   **blow up, blow somebody or something up**
This verb is in *Really Learn 100 Phrasal Verbs*.

6 break something off

Check Use the sentences in the Study box to help you do these exercises.

MEANING

Which of these verbs most closely matches this meaning of *break something off*?

a to discuss
b to start
c to end

GRAMMAR

Which of these are grammatically possible?

a They broke off the talks.
b They broke off them.
c They broke them off.
d The talks were broken off.

→ Now check your answers in the key.

Practise

1 Complete these sentences with the correct form of *break off*.

a Her uncle had _____ all contact with the family.
b The Prime Minister _____ his holiday and flew home to deal with the crisis.
c I decided to _____ our engagement because he had an affair.

2 Read the text from the newspaper. Underline the word that means the same as *break something off* and then rewrite the sentence using *break something off*.

> **PEACE TALKS FAIL** The future of the peace talks seemed in doubt last night after the two sides failed to reach an agreement. Leaders decided to end discussions so that both sides can have a chance to rethink their policies.

→ Now check your answers in the key.

Build your vocabulary

SYNONYMS

The verb **terminate** is a more formal way of saying **break something off**:

▸ We have **terminated** our links with the company.

SIMILAR VERBS

Break off can also be used without an object with the same meaning:

▸ We don't know why the talks **broke off**.

See also **break up** in *Really Learn 100 Phrasal Verbs*.

OTHER MEANINGS

Break off, break off something can also mean 'to stop speaking or doing something suddenly':

▸ He **broke off** in the middle of a sentence.

7 break out

Study Read these sentences carefully.

▸ War **broke out** in 1939.
▸ Fighting sometimes **breaks out** between gangs of youths in the town.
▸ The fire **broke out** in an upstairs bedroom.
▸ A furious political row has **broken out** over the issue of ID cards.

Check Use the sentences in the Study box to help you do these exercises.

MEANING

1 Which of the following verbs means
the same as *break out*?

appear   finish   start

2 One of these could <u>not</u> *break out*.
Which one?

an argument   a disease
a party   a fire   a fight

→ Now check your answers in the key.

GRAMMAR

Which of these are
grammatically possible?

a A fight broke out.
b A fight has broken out.
c A fight has broken it
out.
d A fight was broken out.

Practise

1 Rewrite the following sentences using a form of *break out*, so that the meaning
stays the same.

a The fight started in the middle of the street.

_____

b Trouble erupted between groups of rival football fans.

_____

c A dangerous virus has started among the people living in the camps.

_____

2 Choose <u>two</u> of the words or phrases below and write a sentence using each of
them and a form of *break out*.

riots   a fierce debate   violence   flu

a _____

b _____

→ Now check your answers in the key.

Build your vocabulary

RELATED WORDS   NOUN: ˈ**outbreak** (This is a countable noun.)
▸ the **outbreak** of war
▸ There's been an **outbreak** of flu in the area.

OTHER MEANINGS   People sometimes use 'peace' as the subject of **break out**:
▸ There are signs that peace has **broken out** in the area.

8 break out; break out of something

Study Read these sentences carefully.

- Six prisoners tried to **break out** but were recaptured.
- Two dangerous robbers had **broken out** of jail.
- She wanted to **break out** of her boring life and do something exciting.

Check Use the sentences in the Study box to help you do these exercises.

MEANING

If you *break out*, what do you do?
Choose the best meaning.

a You escape from a place or situation.
b You hurt yourself.
c You get a new job.

GRAMMAR

There is a grammatical mistake in one of these sentences. Can you find it and correct it?

a He broke out of jail.
b He has broken out of jail.
c He will break out of jail.
d He broke out the jail.

→ Now check your answers in the key.

Practise

1 Replace the <u>underlined</u> verbs in the following sentences with an appropriate form of *break out*.

a He tried to <u>get out of</u> the room that he was locked in.
b Five prisoners <u>have escaped from</u> the jail already this year.
c He desperately wanted to <u>get away from</u> his loveless marriage.
d Look at the lock. Nobody broke into this room, but somebody <u>got out</u>.

2 Imagine you are a prison governor. Think about what changes you would make to stop prisoners wanting to escape. Write two or three sentences about it using a form of *break out*.

a _____
b _____
c _____

→ Now check your answers in the key.

Build your vocabulary

RELATED WORDS   NOUN: ˈbreakout (This is a countable noun.)
    ▸ *The governor resigned after several prison **breakouts**.*

OPPOSITES   **break in, break into something**
    This verb is in *Really Learn 100 Phrasal Verbs*.

OTHER MEANINGS   **break something out** means 'to get something ready to be used':
    ▸ *Let's **break out** the food and drink and have fun!*

9 bring something about

- ▸ The oil spill may **bring about** an environmental disaster.
- ▸ They are trying to **bring about** much-needed changes in the law.
- ▸ We want success, but how do we **bring** it **about**?
- ▸ Extreme weather may **be brought about** by global warming.

Check Use the sentences in the Study box to help you do these exercises.

MEANING

Which of the following is closest in meaning to *bring something about*? Choose <u>one</u> answer.

a to change something so it is the opposite of what it was before
b to make something happen
c to happen after something

GRAMMAR

Which of these are grammatically possible?

a Having children brings about big changes.
b Having children brings them about.
c Having children brings about them.
d Big changes are brought about by having children.

→ Now check your answers in the key.

Practise

1 Match the two halves to make complete sentences.

a The introduction of new technology
b What was it that
c What does a teacher have to do
d High interest rates

i   could bring about a recession.
ii brought about mass unemployment.
iii brought about such a change?
iv to bring about improvements in the classroom?

2 Rewrite the following sentences so that the meanings stay the same, using the correct form of *bring something about* and making any other necessary changes.

a Changes in the weather cause changes in our mood.

_____

b The government wants to reduce tobacco consumption.

_____

c The failure of the business happened because of a worldwide recession.

_____

d What made the company collapse?

_____

e Expecting problems can play an important part in making them happen.

_____

→ Now check your answers in the key.

Build your vocabulary

SYNONYMS

cause something:
- ▸ *Most of his problems **were caused** by his job.*

10 bring something back

- Many people think we should **bring back** old-fashioned values.
- Do you agree with **bringing** hanging **back**?
- They've taken music off the programme, but they might **bring** it **back** next month.
- The old system should be **brought back**.

Check Use the sentences in the Study box to help you do these exercises.

MEANING

Complete this meaning of *bring something back* using the words below:

used   existed   again   before

to make sth that _____

or was done _____

be _____ or done

_____

GRAMMAR

Which of these are grammatically possible?

a They should bring back the old rules.

b They should bring back them.

c They should bring the old rules back.

d The old rules should be brought back.

→ Now check your answers in the key.

Practise

1 Complete these sentences using the correct form of *bring something back* and any other words you need.

a Gambling is no longer illegal in Mexico, and casinos are being _____.

b It would be good if they _____ black and white movies.

c Can the country's new leader _____ democracy?

d 'Friends' was my favourite TV show. I wish they'd _____.

2 Complete the responses to the following statements, using a form of *bring back* in your answer, and one of the words below.

national service   beating   it

a I think everyone should spend some time in the armed forces.

   I agree, they should _____.

b The old system was much simpler than this one.

   Why don't you suggest _____?

c There's nothing wrong with punishing kids.

   Next you'll be wanting to _____!

→ Now check your answers in the key.

Build your vocabulary

SYNONYMS   **Restore** and **reintroduce something** mean the same but are more formal:
- *They want to **reintroduce** grants for college students.*

OTHER MEANINGS   **Bring something back** can also refer to memories:
- *The photos **brought back** happy memories of our trip.*

11 bring something down

- The economic recovery will **bring down** unemployment.
- They got rid of staff in order to **bring** costs **down**.
- Taxes are very high and the government has promised to **bring** them **down**.
- The store **brought** the price of the toy **down** to $10.
- They've **brought** prices **down** by 10%.
- The quality of goods has been **brought down** by trying to cut costs.

Check Use the sentences in the Study box to help you do these exercises.

MEANING

Which of these explanations best fits this meaning of *bring something down*?

a to increase the price, number or level of something

b to change the price, number or level of something

c to reduce the price, number or level of something

GRAMMAR

There is a grammatical mistake in one of the following sentences. Find it and correct it.

a They've brought down prices.

b They've brought prices down.

c They've brought prices down at £13.99.

d Prices were brought down by 3%.

→ Now check your answers in the key.

Practise

1 Fill the gaps in these sentences with the correct form of *bring down,* and one of the prepositions below.

by   from   to

a The airline has _____ the cost of flights _____15%.

b We're _____ the price _____ £25.

c They will _____ the price _____ £30 to £25.

2 Rewrite the following sentences so that the meaning stays the same, using a form of *bring something down.*

a Interest rates have been reduced.

_____

b We plan to lower our prices.

_____

c The rate has been reduced by 20%.

_____

→ Now check your answers in the key.

Build your vocabulary

SYNONYMS

The verbs **reduce** and **lower** mean the same as **bring something down** and are used in the same way:

- *The government has promised to **reduce** taxes.*

OPPOSITES

The verb **increase** and the phrasal verb **put something up** mean the opposite.

12 brush something up; brush up on something

Study Read these sentences carefully.

- Dave did a one-week course to **brush up** his Spanish before he went to Chile.
- She's **brushing** her computer skills **up** for the IT test tomorrow.
- I'm worried about my tennis — I need to **brush** it **up** fast.
- She's **brushed up on** her knowledge of history for our trip to Egypt.
- How is your algebra? Do you need to **brush up on** it?

Check Use the sentences in the Study box to help you do these exercises.

MEANING

If you *brush something up* or
brush up on something, do you:

a learn it for the first time?
b revise something you already
know?
c clean something that is dirty?

GRAMMAR

Which of these are
grammatically possible?

a Let's brush up on our
French.
b We brushed up our French.
c I brushed up on it
yesterday.
d His French was brushed up.

→ Now check your answers in the key.

Practise

1 There is *one* mistake in each of the following sentences. Find it and correct it.

a The staff have been brushing it up on what to do when a passenger has a heart
attack.
b Are you brushing up it tonight?
c He will have to brush his writing if he wants to go to college.
d Last year their cooking was terrible but they have brushed up now.

2 Write two or three suggestions of ways to *brush up* your English.

_____

_____

_____

→ Now check your answers in the key.

Build your vocabulary

SYNONYMS

polish something up:

- *We're going to **polish up** our German before the trip to Berlin.*
- *My spelling is terrible — I have to **polish** it **up**.*

You can also use to **revise something** (British English) or to
review something (American English):

- *I've begun **reviewing** my French.*

13 call something off

- Bosses **called off** the meeting which was scheduled for today.
- They **called** the wedding **off** because the bride's mother was seriously ill.
- The strike was planned for Wednesday but they **called** it **off**.
- Several games have **been called off** because of the snow.

Check Use the sentences in the Study box to help you do these exercises.

MEANING

Which of these explanations best fits this meaning of *call something off*?

a to announce that something will happen

b to decide that something will not happen or continue

c to plan for something to happen

GRAMMAR

There is a grammatical mistake in <u>one</u> of these sentences. Find it and correct it.

a They called the search off.

b They called off the search.

c The search called off.

d They called it off.

e The search was called off.

→ Now check your answers in the key.

Practise

1 Fill the gaps in these sentences with the correct form of *call off*.

a The singer has _____ his concerts due to illness.

b The President's visit was _____ for security reasons.

c The search for the missing boy has _____.

d Union leaders say they will _____ a nationwide strike planned for tomorrow.

e The merger _____ at the last minute.

2 You are the manager of a company and have these events in your diary. You are too busy, so decide which events you need to cancel and write a note to your colleagues using a form of *call something off*.

Monday 12th

11.30 Sales meeting

13.00 Drinks reception

13.15 Board meeting

14.00 Factory visit

_____

_____

_____

_____

_____

→ Now check your answers in the key.

Build your vocabulary

SYNONYMS

To **cancel something** means the same:
- It isn't too late to **cancel** the trip.

14 calm down;

calm something, somebody or yourself down

Study Read these sentences carefully.

- ▸ Will everyone please **calm down**! Everything's under control.
- ▸ After the storm, it wasn't long until things **calmed down** again.
- ▸ After **calming** the customer **down**, she quickly solved the problem.
- ▸ The drugs effectively **calm down** the reaction to the sting.
- ▸ She was so stressed that I didn't know how to **calm** her **down**.
- ▸ I was so angry that I had to have a cigarette just to **calm** myself **down**.

Check Use the sentences in the Study box to help you do these exercises.

MEANING

Calm down refers to a situation or a person becoming quiet and peaceful after being noisy, angry, excited, etc. Which of these can *calm down*?

a a still lake
b a very frightened child
c a stormy sea
d somebody listening to quiet music

GRAMMAR

Find and correct any mistakes in the following.

a Stop crying! Be calm down.
b She couldn't calm down herself.
c I was shaking, and had to take deep breaths to calm me down.
d Wait until things calm down a bit.

→ Now check your answers in the key.

Practise

1 There is *one* word missing from each sentence. Add the missing word.

a It can be really difficult calm down an angry child.

b Can you just take a deep breath calm down please?

c Why are the kids rushing around like that? Can't you calm down?

2 Rewrite the sentences using a form of *calm down* and an object (a noun or pronoun) if necessary.

a If you don't stop shouting, I'm going to call the police.

b When I get angry, I listen to my favourite music to make myself feel better.

c The captain did his job and got his team quiet and focused.

→ Now check your answers in the key.

Build your vocabulary

SIMILAR VERBS   To **calm somebody** means the same:
▸ He tried to **calm** the children.

15 clear up; clear something up

Study Read these sentences carefully.
- He was **clearing up** in the kitchen after the meal.
- Who's going to **clear up** the mess in here?
- She **cleared** the broken glass **up**.
- You left all the toys out. You can **clear** them **up**!
- The site is full of old cars and needs to **be cleared up** before we can start building.

Check Use the sentences in the Study box to help you do these exercises.

MEANING

Choose <u>two</u> of these words to complete this meaning of *clear up*.

clean   untidy   dirty   neat

to make something _____
and _____,
especially by putting things in the place where they belong

GRAMMAR

Which of these are grammatically possible?

a I need to clear up.
b I need to clear up the mess.
c I need to clear the mess up.
d I need to clear up it.
e The mess must be cleared up.

→ Now check your answers in the key.

Practise

1 Match the two halves to make complete sentences.

a When I've cleared the lunch things up,
b Everything must be cleared up
c I spend my days clearing up
d I'll just clear up my books
e Until this mess is cleared up,

i after the children.
ii I'm going to stay with my sister.
iii before my parents come home.
iv I'll go out.
v and then I'll be ready.

2 Complete the sentences in an appropriate way, using *clear up* or *clear something up*.

a What a mess there is in here! _____.
b I'll be out of the office for a few days, so I _____.
c People leave waste all over the beach. Who pays _____?

→ Now check your answers in the key.

Build your vocabulary

RELATED WORDS   NOUN: ˈclear-up (This is British English and is usually singular.)
- *After the storm, there was a massive **clear-up** operation.*

SYNONYMS   **Tidy up, tidy something up** is used mainly in British English:
- *Who's going to **tidy up** this mess?*

OTHER MEANINGS   If an illness or infection **clears up** or something **clears it up**, it disappears:
- The rash *cleared up* quickly.

16 clear something **up**

Study Read these sentences carefully.

- I want to **clear up** any misunderstandings.
- Have you got a moment? I just need to **clear** a few details **up**.
- There's been a lot of confusion and we want to **clear** it **up**.
- Many police cases are never **cleared up**.

Check Use the sentences in the Study box to help you do these exercises.

MEANING

1 Which of these explanations best fits this meaning of *clear something up*?

a to talk about something important
b to solve or explain something that is mysterious or confusing

2 Which of these could you <u>not</u> clear up?

doubts   problems   confusion
anger   mysteries   stories

GRAMMAR

Which of these are grammatically possible?

a I'd like to clear up.
b I'd like to clear up any confusion.
c I'd like to clear it up.
d I'd like to clear up it.
e The confusion was cleared up.

→ Now check your answers in the key.

Practise

1 Complete these sentences with the correct form of *clear up*.

a The leaflet aims to _____ any doubts you may have about the product.
b Officially, the murder has never been _____.
c Can we talk? I think we need to _____ a few things.
d I _____ a few points before I started.
e This misunderstanding will have to _____.
f Police have never _____ the mystery of her disappearance.
g We'll try to _____ any problems you may have with your new computer.

2 Choose two of the words below, and write sentences using them and a form of *clear up*.

confusion   doubts   queries   mistakes   misunderstanding   mystery

a _____
b _____

→ Now check your answers in the key.

Build your vocabulary

RELATED WORDS   NOUN: ˈclear-up (This is used in British English, often as an adjective.)
- *Police chiefs say that crime **clear-up** rates are rising.*

SYNONYMS   **Solve** can be used for crimes, problems and mysteries:
- *The police have not yet **solved** the case.*

17 come up against somebody or something

Study Read these sentences carefully.

▸ People sometimes **come up against** prejudice in the workplace.
▸ He **came up against** many dangers during his life.
▸ The law can be a frightening process if you've never **come up against** it before.
▸ Chelsea are one of the toughest teams we've **come up against**.

Check Use the sentences in the Study box to help you do these exercises.

MEANING

1 If you *come up against somebody or something*, which of the following is true?

a you arrive somewhere
b you have to deal with something difficult
c you have no difficulties at all

2 Which of the following things could you *come up against*? More than one answer is correct.

a a problem   **d** resistance
b a solution   **e** an answer
c a sports team   **f** a difficulty

GRAMMAR

Which of these are grammatically possible?

a I've come up against a problem.
b We came up it against.
c We came up against it.
d A problem was come up against.

→ Now check your answers in the key.

Practise

1 Fill the gaps in these sentences with the correct form of *come up against* and any other words you need.

a I _____ a question which I couldn't answer.

b They will _____ some very stiff competition.

c We didn't _____ any unexpected hurdles.

d We _____ the problem of transporting the cake.

e The course will prepare you for any situations you are likely _____.

f We introduce difficult grammar early as you will _____ sooner or later.

2 Think of a difficult situation you have been in. Write a sentence about it using the verb *come up against somebody or something*.

_____

→ Now check your answers in the key.

Build your vocabulary

IDIOMS

Come up against a brick wall means 'to be unable to make any progress because of a problem':
▸ *I've been trying to research my family history but I've **come up** against a brick wall.*

SYNONYMS

Encounter is more formal:
▸ *We **encountered** a number of difficulties in the first week.*

18 come up with something

Check Use the sentences in the Study box to help you do these exercises.

MEANING

Come up with means to think of an idea, especially to answer a question or solve a problem. Which <u>one</u> of the following are you <u>not</u> likely to *come up with*?

a a solution
b an answer
c a problem
d a better proposal
e an alternative design

→ Now check your answers in the key.

GRAMMAR

Which of the following are grammatically possible?

a He came up with a new idea.
b He came up with it.
c What was come up with?
d What a good idea. Who came it up?

Practise

1 Use appropriate forms of *come up with* to join two parts and make six sentences.

a The architect was asked to _____		**i** good ideas.
b What's the best idea you _____		**ii** two different designs for the house.
c Jack is really good at _____		**iii** a suitable name for their baby.
d The government has _____		**iv** new proposals for tackling crime.
e Have you _____		**v** anything yet?
f New parents often find it really difficult to _____		**vi** so far?

2 Rewrite these sentences using suitable forms of *come up with*.

a My wife's brilliant at inventing new recipes.

_____

b Hey, listen to this. I've just thought of a really good joke.

_____

c Let me know if you think of anything else.

_____

d We've got to find a solution as soon as possible.

_____

→ Now check your answers in the key.

19 consist of something

- ▸ Football teams **consist of** 11 players, and rugby teams of 15.
- ▸ It's an amazing place, **consisting of** about 100 beautiful temples.
- ▸ A healthy breakfast **consists of** cereal and low-fat milk, with freshly squeezed orange juice.
- ▸ My typical day at work **consisted** mainly **of** answering the telephone.

Check Use the sentences in the Study box to help you do these exercises.

MEANING

True or false?

a We can use **consist of** to say *how many parts* something has. _____

b We can use **consist of** to say *what happens* at a meeting or an event.

_____

c Adverbs must go *after* **consist of**.

_____

GRAMMAR

Which of these sentences are grammatically possible?

a The country consists of 7,000 islands.

b The house consists 10 rooms of.

c What does it consist of?

d 7,000 islands are consisted of by the country.

→ Now check your answers in the key.

Practise

1 *Contain* or *consist of*? *Contain* and *consist of* are similar, but not the same. Read the two examples, then decide which is correct in each of the sentences below.

Chocolate **contains** a lot of fat. (= there is fat *inside* it)

The course **consists of** lectures, seminars and exams. (= the *parts* that make the course)

a Warning: this cake *consists of/contains* nuts.

b Great Britain *consists of/contains* 3 countries: England, Scotland and Wales.

c These days my weekends usually *consist of/contain* sitting in front of the TV, and not much else!

d Police suspected that the suitcase *consisted of/contained* stolen goods.

2 Match the two halves to make complete sentences.

a They have a very simple diet,

b This year's conference consists

c Not everyone knows this, but the human body

i mainly of guest presentations.

ii consists mostly of water.

iii consisting of rice and fish.

→ Now check your answers in the key.

Build your vocabulary

SYNONYMS

To **be made up of**:

- ▸ *The necklace **was made up of** hundreds of coloured glass beads.*

To **comprise** means the same, but is more formal:

- ▸ *The country **comprises** no less than 7,000 islands.*

20 count on somebody or something

Study Read these sentences carefully.

▸ The shop is **counting on** people buying hundreds of these toys.
▸ I know you need a good report and you can **count on** me to write it.
▸ I hadn't **counted on** them arriving early!
▸ You think a lot of people will come in tomorrow, but don't **count on** it.
▸ Gustav can be **counted on** to win his game.

Check Use the sentences in the Study box to help you do these exercises.

MEANING

If you can *count on somebody or something,* which one of the following is not true?

a You expect them to do something.
b You trust them to do something.
c You request them to do something.

GRAMMAR

Which of these are grammatically possible?

a You can count on me.
b You can count me on.
c You can count on Gary to help.
d I didn't count Gary coming.
e Gary can always be counted on.

→ Now check your answers in the key.

Practise

1 **Put the words in the correct order to make sentences.**

a the create on we jobs new counting to of thousands factory are

_____

b can support you count on public's the

_____

c on don't before him arriving 7 p.m. count

_____

2 **Rewrite the parts of the following sentences in brackets so that the meaning stays the same, using an appropriate form of *count on* and any other words you need.**

a If you get in a difficult situation (you can always trust us) to help you.

_____

b (I'm not planning on getting) any help from my family.

_____

c Where's Jack? (I was expecting him to be here).

_____

→ Now check your answers in the key.

Build your vocabulary

SIMILAR VERBS

You can also use **bank on** with a similar meaning:

▸ *The ski resorts are **banking on** having a lot of snow this year.*

Depend on, rely on, calculate on and **reckon on** (more informal) also have a similar meaning:

▸ *I was **relying on** you to bring the keys!*
▸ *We didn't **reckon on** the other team being so strong.*

21 do away with something or somebody

Study Read these sentences carefully.
- ▸ They decided to **do away with** their garage and turn it into an office.
- ▸ Computers **have done away with** a lot of the repetitive work.
- ▸ By bringing new technology into schools, we are not trying to **do away with** teachers.
- ▸ They might change the system, or **do away with** it altogether.
- ▸ History cannot **be done away with**.

Check Use the sentences in the Study box to help you do these exercises.

MEANING

Do away with something or somebody means to get rid of it/them a) by deciding not to have or do it/them any more *or* b) by making it no longer necessary. Say whether a) *or* b) applies in the following sentences.

a The company has done away with its bonus system.
b The new treatment could do away with the need for surgery.
c We could do away with a lot of our paperwork.

GRAMMAR

Correct the mistakes in these sentences:

a They did away their garage.
b They did it away with.
c They did the garage away with.
d The garage was done away.

→ Now check your answers in the key.

Practise

1 Match the two halves to make complete sentences.
  a The invention of printing
  b Working from home
  c Recycling
  i can do away with a lot of household waste.
  ii did away with the need for handwritten books.
  iii does away with time wasted travelling to work.

2 Complete the following sentences using a form of *do away with* and one of the words or phrases below.

secrecy   it   hunting   these outdated laws

a The shed was falling down so we decided to _____.
b He is against killing foxes and thinks we should _____.
c We believe in freedom of information and want to _____.
d It is time that _____.

→ Now check your answers in the key.

Build your vocabulary

SYNONYMS

To **abolish something** is a more formal verb meaning 'to get rid of something':
- ▸ *These outdated laws should **be abolished**.*

To **eliminate** or **end something** are more formal verbs meaning 'to make something unnecessary':
- ▸ *The software can reduce or **eliminate** paperwork.*

22 do without; do without somebody or something

Study Read these sentences carefully.

▸ We haven't got any milk. You'll have to **do without**.
▸ When there wasn't enough food, they simply **did without**.
▸ He's so helpful, I couldn't **do without** him.
▸ I use my laptop so much, I don't know how I ever **did without** it!

Check Use the sentences in the Study box to help you do these exercises.

MEANING

Which of these explanations best fits the meaning of *do without*?

a to ask for help
b to get rid of somebody or something
c to manage without somebody or something

GRAMMAR

There is a grammatical mistake in one of these sentences. Find it and correct it.

a I couldn't do without him.
b I couldn't do without a secretary.
c I couldn't do it without.
d You'll have to do without.

→ Now check your answers in the key.

Practise

1 Rearrange the words to make correct sentences.

a have to enough If without there's not do you'll

_____

b TV without couldn't We afford so did a we

_____

c there without did enough wasn't I because

_____

2 Decide which of the things in the box is most important to you, and then write one or two sentences using *do without*, saying why you could not manage without it.

mobile phone/cellphone   MP3 player   washing machine
newspaper   hairdryer

a _____
b _____

→ Now check your answers in the key.

Build your vocabulary

SYNONYMS

Go without means the same as **do without**:
▸ *I'm hungry because I **went without** breakfast this morning.*

OTHER MEANINGS

Can/could do without is often used when something is annoying you because you do not want it:
▸ *I **could have done without** all this hassle.*
▸ *I could really **do without** my manager criticizing me all the time.*
▸ *That's the sort of comment I can really **do without**!*

23 drop out; drop out of something

Study Read these sentences carefully.

- Alice was going to lead the expedition but she **dropped out** after two days.
- Richard started studying French but he soon **dropped out of** the course.
- The company is going to **drop out of** the deal because the costs are too high.
- Higher education is important, and we are trying to prevent students **dropping out of** it.
- He left his job in New York, moved to a Pacific island, and **dropped out**.

Check Use the sentences in the Study box to help you do these exercises.

MEANING

Which one of these is not an answer to the question: If somebody *drops out (of something)*, what do they do?

a They stop doing an activity before it has ended.
b They leave normal society to lead a very different life.
c They get angry about something.
d They leave a group or an organisation.

GRAMMAR

Which of these are grammatically possible?

a I'm going to drop out because the course is boring.
b They dropped him out of the course.
c Just finish the course — don't drop out!
d The course was dropped out of.

→ Now check your answers in the key.

Practise

1 Replace the words that are <u>underlined</u> with an appropriate form of *drop out* or *drop out of*.

a How many people <u>have left</u> the course after the summer holidays?
b She told me that if the lessons get too difficult, she's <u>going to give up</u>.
c There was a massive argument between the coach and the players and seven of them <u>stopped playing for</u> the team.
d Unfortunately <u>we have to withdraw from</u> the competition.

2 Write one or two sentences in answer to this question, using forms of *drop out* or *drop out of something* where you can.

Have you or has somebody you know ever dropped out of something? Why?

_____

_____

→ Now check your answers in the key.

Build your vocabulary

RELATED WORDS   NOUN: ˈ**drop-out.** This is usually a countable noun and means a person who leaves school, college or a course before the end. In the USA, children who leave High School without graduating are known as 'high school drop-outs':

- *He is now a prizewinning author, despite once being a **high school drop-out**.*
- *The physics course has a really high **drop-out rate**. I think it's just too difficult.*

24 eat something up (1)

Study Read these sentences carefully.

▸ My housemates had **eaten up** all the food in the house!
▸ **Eat** your dinner **up**, Joe.
▸ It was a huge piece of cake but she **ate** it all **up**.
▸ All the party food had been **eaten up**.
▸ I've got a salad which needs **eating up**.

Check Use the sentences in the Study box to help you do these exercises.

MEANING

If you *eat something up*, which <u>one</u> of the following statements could be true?

a There is none left on your plate.
b There is some on your plate.
c You haven't eaten anything.

GRAMMAR

Which of these are grammatically possible?

a I ate up all my dinner.
b I ate it all up.
c I ate all my dinner up.
d I had eaten it all up.
e I ate all it up.

→ Now check your answers in the key.

Practise

1 Choose the correct form of *eat something up* to fill the gaps in the sentences. You will not need to use all of them.

ate it all up   eat up   eating it up   ate up   eating up   eats it up   eaten up

a I _____ all my dinner because I was so hungry.
b My Gran always made us _____ our greens.
c Who has _____ all this cake?
d This food needs _____ .
e I love chocolate so I _____ .

2 Complete these sentences in a suitable way, using a form of *eat up* and any other words you need.

a I really liked the cheesecake so _____ .
b He wasn't hungry so _____ .
c There was a whole bar of chocolate here five minutes ago. Who _____
_____ ?

→ Now check your answers in the key.

Build your vocabulary

SIMILAR VERBS   **Eat up** can also be used without an object to tell somebody to eat all of something, especially to eat quickly:
▸ *Come on kids, **eat up**! We need to leave in a minute.*

OTHER MEANINGS   In American English you can use **eat something up** to mean that somebody really likes something (not food) and wants more of it:
▸ *He started telling jokes and the audience just **ate it up**.*

25 eat something up (2)

Study Read these sentences carefully.

▸ The rent **eats up** more than half of his salary.
▸ Doing housework **eats** a lot of my time **up**.
▸ The van just **eats up** gas.
▸ I got some money for my birthday, but my parking fine has **eaten** most of it **up**.
▸ A large part of the profits had been **eaten up** by unexpected costs.

Check Use the sentences in the Study box to help you do these exercises.

MEANING

Which of these explanations best fits this meaning of *eat something up*?

a to lose something
b to use a lot of something that you want to keep
c to spend money

GRAMMAR

Which of these are grammatically possible?

a Rent eats up a lot of my income.
b Rent eats a lot of it up.
c Rent eats a lot of my income up.
d Rent eats it a lot up.
e A lot of my income is eaten up by rent.

→ Now check your answers in the key.

Practise

1 Fill the gaps in these sentences with a suitable form of *eat up*.

a This program _____ huge amounts of computer memory.
b Most of my income _____ by bills.
c Work _____ too much of my time!
d Legal costs _____ all the savings I had.

2 Look at the chart, which shows how Jane spends her money. Write two sentences using a form of *eat something up*, showing how the money is spent.

→ Now check your answers in the key.

Build your vocabulary

SYNONYMS   The verb **consume** is a more formal way of saying **eat something up**:
▸ *Looking after children **consumes** a lot of time.*

OTHER MEANINGS If something **eats somebody up**, they can't think of anything else:
▸ *He was **eaten up** by jealousy.*

26 face up to somebody or something

Study Read these sentences carefully.
- She has to **face up to** her problem and do something about it.
- **Face up to** it — we are never going to win.
- My boss is quite aggressive, but I don't have the courage to **face up to** him.
- We must **face up to** the fact that things are not going to get better.
- **Facing up to** what you have done takes courage.
- The problem has got to be **faced up to** because we can't ignore it forever.

Check Use the sentences in the Study box to help you do these exercises.

MEANING

If you tell somebody to *face up to* something, are you asking them to:

a tell everyone about a difficult or bad situation?
b end a difficult or bad situation?
c accept and deal with a difficult or bad situation?

GRAMMAR

Which of these are grammatically possible?

a We have to face up to the problem.
b We have to face it up to.
c We must face up to it.
d The situation has to be faced up to.

→ Now check your answers in the key.

Practise

1 Which of these sentences contain the phrasal verb *face up to something*?

a He is bravely facing up to his mistake.
b He doesn't know what sentence he will get, but he's facing up to 15 years in jail.
c These are the kind of problems every workplace has to face up to.
d There she was, face up to the sun on the beach.
e The card was turned face up to the audience.

2 Complete these sentences with an appropriate form of *face up to*.

a I want him _____ the fact that he cannot leave his job.
b He won't _____ his responsibilities as a father.
c We are starting _____ life without our star player in the team.
d _____ your problems is an important part of overcoming them.
e You are not _____ the fact that we don't have enough money to buy a new house.
f When will you _____ reality and ask for your parents' help?

→ Now check your answers in the key.

Build your vocabulary

SYNONYMS

Square up to something means the same:
- You must **square up to** the reality of being out of work.

27 fall back on something or somebody

Study Read these sentences carefully.

- ▶ He was forced to **fall back on** his savings when he lost his job.
- ▶ She **fell back on** the only excuse she could think of.
- ▶ When his writing career failed, he **fell back on** teaching.
- ▶ Save some money and then you can **fall back on** it when times are hard.
- ▶ If this business fails, she will have nothing to **fall back on**.

Check Use the sentences in the Study box to help you do these exercises.

MEANING

Which of these explanations best fits the meaning of *fall back on something or somebody*?

a to ask for help
b to use something or somebody when the situation is difficult
c to stop making any progress

GRAMMAR

Which of these are grammatically possible?

a I had to fall back on my savings.
b I fell back on them.
c Her savings were fallen back on.

→ Now check your answers in the key.

Practise

1 Match the two halves to make complete sentences.

a If I don't get this job,
b I kept my old computer so
c I couldn't think of what to say so
d Save some money, then

i I fell back on my usual silence.
ii I had something to fall back on if the new one went wrong.
iii you'll always have something to fall back on.
iv I still have the other one to fall back on.

2 Complete the gaps in these sentences using the correct form of *fall back on*.

a When my business failed, I _____ my father for help.
b If I spend this money, I will have nothing to _____.
c I didn't know what to talk about so I _____ the weather.
d I tried some exciting new exercises with the students, but ended up _____ old favourites.

→ Now check your answers in the key.

Build your vocabulary

RELATED WORDS   NOUN: ¹**fallback** (This is a countable noun.)
- ▶ *This restaurant is a good **fallback** if the other one is full.*
- ▶ *I haven't got the **fallback** option of my sister now she's moved to Australia.*

SYNONYMS   **Fall back upon** is more formal:
- ▶ *You know you can **fall back upon** the support of your family.*
- ▶ *In his later years, the artist **fell back upon** poetry and music.*

28 fall for something

Study Read these sentences carefully.

▶ Don't **fall for** her lies — she'll tell you anything to make you feel sorry for her.
▶ He told you he's famous and you believed him? I can't believe you **fell for** it!
▶ She just cries to try to get what she wants — and her father **falls for** it every time!
▶ What a stupid trick to **fall for**!

Check Use the sentences in the Study box to help you do these exercises.

MEANING

1 **If somebody tells you something and you
fall for it,**

  a do they tell you something that is
    true or untrue?
  b do you believe it?

2 **Which one object cannot go with fall for?**

  a a lie
  b the truth
  c a trick

GRAMMAR

**Which of these are grammatically
possible?**

  a A lot of people fell for his story.
  b His story was fallen for by a lot
    of people.
  c You didn't fall for that, did you?
  d You didn't fall that for, did you?
  e She was too smart to fall for a lie
    like that.

→ Now check your answers in the key.

Practise

Rewrite the words in *italics* in the following sentences using a suitable form of *fall
for* and any other words you need.

a You don't think *I'm stupid enough to believe that,* do you?

_____

b *I believed the advert on TV* and bought three, but they all broke!

_____

c *Everyone accepted all the propaganda,* even though most of it was not true.

_____

d He tried to fool his insurance company and said that this phone had been stolen,
but they rejected his false claim.

_____

e *I'm not the sort of parent who takes any notice of the argument* that 'everyone else
has got one'.

_____

→ Now check your answers in the key.

Build your vocabulary

SIMILAR VERBS   **take somebody in**. These two sentences mean the same:
    ▶ He **took** lots of people **in** with his lies.
    ▶ Lots of people **fell for** his lies.

OTHER MEANINGS   To **fall for somebody** means to fall in love with somebody, or to
    start to find them very attractive:
    ▶ I totally **fell for him** the first time we met.

29 fall out; fall out with somebody

Study Read these sentences carefully.

- The two men have **fallen out**.
- He resigned after **falling out** with his boss.
- They **fell out** over their father's will.
- Let's sort this out. I don't want to **fall out** with you.
- Don't **fall out** over it. It's not worth it.

Check Use the sentences in the Study box to help you do these exercises.

MEANING

If you *fall out* with somebody, which of these statements is true?

a You have argued with them and do not like them now.
b You have always been good friends.
c You speak to them because you want something.

GRAMMAR

There is a mistake in <u>one</u> of these sentences. Find it and correct it.

a They fell out with each other.
b They fell out over money.
c They fell out with each other over money.
d They fell out with money.
e He fell out with his brother.

→ Now check your answers in the key.

Practise

1 Choose the correct preposition(s) to complete these sentences. You will not need them all.

with   over   to   of

a He left home after he fell out _____ his parents.

b It's silly to fall out _____ such a small thing.

c I fell out _____ him _____ a project that we were both working on.

2 Complete the dialogue in a suitable way, using a form of *fall out* in each sentence, one of the phrases below and any other words you need.

the time for my tutorial   you   my tutor

a I heard that you've changed your course now? Why?

_____.

b Really? What was it all about?

_____.

c That sounds a very silly thing to argue about!
Careful! _____.

→ Now check your answers in the key.

Build your vocabulary

RELATED WORDS   NOUN: **a ˌfalling-ˈout** (This is usually singular.)
- *He resigned after a **falling-out** with the committee.*

30 fit in; fit in with somebody or something

Study Read these sentences carefully.

▸ Jane should **fit in** OK and be happy in her new school.
▸ She's a good worker, but she isn't **fitting in** here.
▸ He left his job because he didn't **fit in with** the rest of the staff.
▸ Tony **fits in** well **with** the other players in the team.

Check Use the sentences in the Study box to help you do these exercises.

MEANING
Which of the following is not an explanation of *fit in*?

a to be suitable in a place
b to be a comfortable member of a group
c to join a new group

GRAMMAR
Which of these sentences are grammatically possible?

a He fits in well with the team.
b He fits in.
c Did Jack fit in with the team?
d He was fit in the team very well.

→ Now check your answers in the key.

Practise

1 Complete the sentences with the correct form of *fit in* or *fit in with*.

a After a while you will _____ the other students.

b I don't know what I can do _____ .

c He felt he _____ after he got to know a few people.

d I wish we hadn't appointed Mike. He doesn't really _____ here.

2 Have you ever had problems *fitting in*? Write a sentence, using a form of *fit in* or *fit in with*.

_____

→ Now check your answers in the key.

Build your vocabulary

SIMILAR VERBS
Fit into something has the same meaning:
▸ She's *fitted into* the team well.

OTHER MEANINGS
Fit in can also mean 'to have a particular role or part in a plan or situation':
▸ *OK, I understand what you want to do, but where do I **fit in**?*

If an activity **fits in with something** else, the two things happen together in an easy or convenient way:
▸ *My job **fits in with** looking after a family.*

If you **fit in with somebody or something**, you adapt to what they are planning or to how they do things:
▸ *I'm easy. I'll **fit in with** whatever you want to do.*

31 fit somebody or something in;
fit somebody or something into something

Study Read these sentences carefully.

- ▶ I have an hour tomorrow when I can **fit** two more patients **in**.
- ▶ Can we manage to **fit in** another appointment this afternoon?
- ▶ I need to see the visitors — can we **fit** them **in** after lunch?
- ▶ I've got so much work to do I don't know how I'm going to **fit** it all **in** by 5 o'clock.
- ▶ Several training sessions need to **be fitted in** next week.
- ▶ How do you manage to **fit** so much **into** your day?

Check Use the sentences in the Study box to help you do these exercises.

MEANING

Which is the best explanation of this meaning of *fit somebody or something in*?

a to find a time to do something or to meet somebody

b to provide a room or a place large enough to put somebody/something

GRAMMAR

Which of these sentences are grammatically possible?

a How many interviews can we fit in tomorrow?

b Can you fit him in an appointment tomorrow?

c I think there's time to fit everyone in.

d Is the meeting fit in?

e Was the meeting fitted in?

> Now check your answers in the key.

Practise

Rewrite the parts of the sentences *in italics* so that the meaning stays the same, using *fit in* and an object (a noun or pronoun).

a I am at a conference all day *so I can't find time to see you*.

b *We have time for five appointments* between 11 and 6.

2 Read Dr Stanley's description of his day tomorrow. When can he *fit in* a half-hour meeting with a new patient? Write the answer using a form of *fit something in*.

> **Memo**
>
> I will get to the office at nine. I have an important meeting for the next three hours and then a business lunch for half an hour. After lunch I will be visiting the hospital until two and then for an hour and a half I will be interviewing some job candidates. I will be going home at five but for my last half hour I am having a telephone discussion with a doctor in Toronto.

> Now check your answers in the key.

Build your vocabulary

OTHER MEANINGS **Fit something in, fit something into something** can also mean 'to find room for something':

- ▶ There's so much in my suitcase that I can't **fit** my shoes **in**.

32 get around to something;
get around to doing something

Study Read these sentences carefully.

▸ Now I'm finally **getting around to** the point of my article.
▸ I keep meaning to put the picture up in my office, but I haven't **got around to** it yet.
▸ She had to wait three hours before the doctor **got around to** her.
▸ When were you going to **get around to** telling me you were leaving?

Check Use the sentences in the Study box to help you do these exercises.

MEANING

When you *get around to* something, do you:

a go and visit somebody?
b write the final paragraph of a report?
c find time to do something?

GRAMMAR

Which of these are grammatically possible?

a I haven't got around to it yet.
b I haven't got around to doing it yet.
c I haven't got around to do it yet.
d I haven't got around it to yet.
e It hasn't been got around to yet.

→ Now check your answers in the key.

Practise

1 Make **five** sentences by joining two parts with a suitable form of *get around to*.

a It's time to get rid of our old car, but we _____
b I should have done the report last week and I'm only just _____
c My sister hasn't been in touch for ages, but I expect she _____
d When are you going to _____
e I really enjoyed her first novel, but I don't think she _____

i writing a second.
ii writing it now.
iii selling it yet.
iv telling him the truth?
v calling me soon.

2 Write two or three sentences about things you should have done but haven't had time to do yet, using a form of *get around to* in each.

_____

_____

_____

→ Now check your answers in the key.

Build your vocabulary

SYNONYMS   In British English, **get round to** is more common.

33 get away with something

Study Read these sentences carefully.

- ▸ Some drivers still think they can **get away with** drinking and driving.
- ▸ The new law means that employers can no longer **get away with** underpaying employees.
- ▸ I know what you've done. You're not **getting away with** this.
- ▸ I can't believe he insulted the boss and **got away with** it.

Check Use the sentences in the Study box to help you do these exercises.

MEANING

Which of these explanations best fits this meaning of *get away with*?

a to escape from somewhere
b to not be punished for something wrong that you have done
c to be punished because you have done something wrong

GRAMMAR

Which of these are grammatically possible?

a He gets away with everything.
b He got away with everything.
c He got it away with.
d He got away with it.

→ Now check your answers in the key.

Practise

1 Fill the gaps in the sentences with the correct form of *get away with*.

a Don't be tempted to cheat — you won't _____ it.
b He _____ everything and his wife never complains.
c He would have _____ it if his brother hadn't told his parents.
d I wouldn't pay if I thought I could _____ it.

2 Read each sentence and then write a sentence saying whether somebody *got away with* something or not.

a She was fined £1 000 for not paying her taxes.

_____

b He stole some money but no one discovered it.

_____

c The kids drew all over the walls and their mother shouted at them.

_____

d He touched the ball with his hand, but the referee didn't notice.

_____

→ Now check your answers in the key.

Build your vocabulary

IDIOMS

get away with murder. To do whatever you want without being stopped or punished:

▸ *She lets the kids **get away with murder** .*

34 get by

Study Read these sentences carefully.

- We're just **getting by** and don't have any money to spare.
- I couldn't cook but I **got by** by getting takeaways.
- Some people can **get by** on less than five hours' sleep.
- He's so helpful, I couldn't **get by** without him.
- I don't know much Japanese, but I can **get by**.

Check Use the sentences in the Study box to help you do these exercises.

MEANING

Which of these explanations best fits this meaning of *get by*?

a to ask somebody to come and help you do something

b to borrow some money in order to buy things

c to manage to live or do something using just what you have

GRAMMAR

There is a grammatical mistake in one of the following sentences. Find it and correct it.

a She earns such a small salary. How does she get by?

b How do they get by on such a small salary?

c How do they get by to such a small salary?

d They got by on her small salary.

→ Now check your answers in the key.

Practise

1 Fill the gaps in these sentences with the correct form of *get by* and, if necessary, one of the prepositions in the box.

on   with   without

a He hopes his family will _____ until he finds another job.

b Many families are struggling to _____ state benefits.

c I don't know how they _____ £8 000 a year.

d I couldn't _____ a computer now.

e We _____ no car for years.

2 Look at the things below and write a sentence for each of them, using a form of *get by*, to say whether you could live without them or not.

MP3 player   washing machine   computer   mobile phone/cellphone   diary/calendar

a _____.

b _____.

c _____.

d _____.

e _____.

→ Now check your answers in the key.

Build your vocabulary

SYNONYMS   The verb **survive** means almost the same as **get by**:
- *Some people have to sell possessions just to **survive**.*

35 get somebody down

Study Read these sentences carefully.

- ▶ I don't know what's **getting** Andy **down** at the moment. He's always complaining.
- ▶ His financial problems began to **get** him **down**.
- ▶ There are times when this job **gets** you **down**.
- ▶ Their constant arguing is really **getting** me **down**.

Check Use the sentences in the Study box to help you do these exercises.

MEANING

If something *gets* you *down*, how does it make you feel?

a bored
b unhappy
c excited

GRAMMAR

Which of these are grammatically possible?

a My problems were getting me down.
b My problems got me down.
c My problems started to get me down.
d I was got down by my problems.

→ Now check your answers in the key.

Practise

1 Match the two halves of these dialogues.

a What's wrong with Guy?
b Do you have trouble walking?
c You look tired. Are you OK?

i Yes, but I don't let it get me down.
ii I'm having problems at work and it's getting me down.
iii His job situation is getting him down.

2 You have received this email from a friend. Write a sentence using *get somebody down*, saying what is making her unhappy.

_____

_____

_____

_____

⊖ ⊖ ⊖	Hello — Inbox	⊂⊃

Delete Junk   Reply Reply All Forward   Print

From: Jane
Subject: Hello
Date: 12 June 2009 15:15:42 GMT
To: sam@free-mail.net

Hi Sam. How are you? I haven't been feeling so good recently. I lost my job six months ago and haven't been able to find another one. I've now got money worries which are making me feel really fed up and miserable. I hope things are better with you!
Jane

3 What *gets* you *down*? Write two sentences using a form of *get somebody down*, saying two things that make you unhappy.

_____

_____

→ Now check your answers in the key.

Build your vocabulary

SYNONYMS

To **depress somebody** is a more formal verb:

- ▶ *Bad weather always **depresses** me.*
- ▶ *It **depresses** me to see him wasting his life.*

36 get over something

▸ If you want to be a singer, you have to **get over** your shyness.
▸ We couldn't find anywhere to live, but we **got over** that by staying with relatives.
▸ This problem can be **got over** without too much difficulty.

Check Use the sentences in the Study box to help you do these exercises.

MEANING

Which of the following is closest in meaning to *get over something*?

a climb over something
b deal with something
c run away from something

GRAMMAR

Which of these are grammatically possible?

a We got over the problem.
b We got over it.
c We got the problem over.
d We got it over.
e The problem was got over.

→ Now check your answers in the key.

Practise

1 **Sarah needs to hand in her homework tomorrow morning. Her computer has broken and she cannot use it to finish her work. Which of the following are ways of *getting over* her problem?**

a She does not do her homework.
b She uses her friend's computer to do her homework.
c She writes her homework on paper.
d She stops worrying about not being able to do her homework.

2 **Complete the following sentences using a form of *get over* and one of the words or expressions below.**

his fear of heights   bad driving habits   your nerves   it

a A large part of the advanced driving test is _____.

b If you get anxious before an exam, deep breathing exercises can help you _____

_____ .

c At first he found talking about his feelings difficult, but he soon _____

_____ .

d He will not be a firefighter until he _____.

→ Now check your answers in the key.

Build your vocabulary

SYNONYMS   To **overcome something** is more formal:
▸ *It was a very difficult problem to* **overcome**.

OTHER MEANINGS   Phrases like *I can't get over it!* are used when you are very surprised or shocked about something:
▸ *I can't get over how much she's changed.*

SIMILAR VERBS   → GET SOMETHING OVER, GET SOMETHING OVER WITH

See also **get over somebody or something** in *Really Learn 100 Phrasal Verbs*.

37 get something **over**; get something **over with**

Study Read these sentences carefully.

- Go to the doctor and **get** the blood test **over**.
- Let's start the job today and then we'll **get** it **over** quickly.
- I'm just pleased that I have **got** the exam **over with**!
- I told him the bad news immediately and **got** it **over with**.

Check Use the sentences in the Study box to help you do these exercises.

MEANING

If you *get something over* or *get
something over with*, do you:

a start something new?
b do something unpleasant and finish it?
c do something pleasant and finish it?
d recover from something?

GRAMMAR

Which of these are grammatically
possible?

a I'm pleased I've got the test over.
b I'm pleased I've got the test over
with.
c I'm pleased I've got over the test.
d Tell him and get it over with.
e Tell him now and then it is got
over with.

→ Now check your answers in the key.

Practise

1 **Match the two halves to make complete sentences.**

a He's been at his desk all morning
b John ate his broccoli in one go and
c He's doing the first dive because
d If Tracy didn't watch TV after school,

i to try to get his paperwork over with.
ii he wants to get it over with.
iii she'd get her homework over by six o'clock.
iv got it over with.

2 **Rewrite the words in *italics* in the following sentences, using the correct form of
get over with and any other words you need.**

a The doctor always gives the painful injections first *to finish them* at the
beginning.

_____

b *Do the housework* this morning and then you can relax this afternoon.

_____

c Tara and Will agreed to be the first people on the list because *they wanted to do
the test and finish it quickly*.

_____

d Hurry up! Tell me my results *and finish it*!

_____

→ Now check your answers in the key.

Build your vocabulary

IDIOMS

get something over and done with. This is a common idiom:
- *Do the test as soon as possible and **get it over and done with**.*

38 give in; give in to somebody or something

Study Read these sentences carefully.

- After he asked me on a date for the fifth time, I **gave in** and said yes.
- She **gives in to** the kids too easily.
- They **gave in to** all the kidnapper's demands.
- If he asks you for money, don't **give in to** him.
- You're trying to blackmail me and I'm not **giving in to** it.

Check Use the sentences in the Study box to help you do these exercises.

MEANING

1 If you *give in to somebody*, do you:

  a do what they want immediately, because you are very happy to do it?

  b do it even though you do not really want to?

2 Two children keep asking their mother for ice cream. Which of these is an example of the mother *giving in to* the children?

  a She does not buy them any.

  b At first she says they cannot have ice cream but she finally says they can.

  c She has earlier promised that if the children are good she will buy them ice cream. They have been good, so she buys them some.

GRAMMAR

Which of these are grammatically possible?

  a She gave in to his demands.

  b She gave in to him.

  c She gave in to it.

  d She gave him in to.

  e She gave in.

→ Now check your answers in the key.

Practise

1 Match the two halves to make complete sentences.

  a If he tries to persuade you to have a cigarette, don't

  b There have been threats on the judge's life, but he says that he will not

  c She is so afraid of her boss that she

  d Management finally

  e He considers talking to the activists to be

  i gives in to him all the time.

  ii gave in to the workers' demands.

  iii give in to temptation.

  iv giving in to terrorism.

  v give in to pressure.

2 Complete the following sentences with a form of *give in (to somebody or something)* and any other other words you need.

  a He asked me so many times to borrow my car that I _____.

  b I'm a very strong person and I don't _____.

  c If you pressure somebody for long enough, they will usually _____.

→ Now check your answers in the key.

Build your vocabulary

OPPOSITES   **hold out against somebody or something:**

       - *The employers are still **holding out against** the striking workers' demands.*

39 go down (1)

Read these sentences carefully.

- His act **went down** very well with the audience.
- The joke **went down** badly.
- You're missing the meeting? I can't see that **going down** too well.
- How did the news **go down** with your parents?

Check Use the sentences in the Study box to help you do these exercises.

MEANING

Choose the explanation that best fits this meaning of *go down.*

a if something **goes down**, it is a failure
b if something **goes down** in a particular way, that is what people think of it
c if something **goes down**, it is very popular

GRAMMAR

Which of these are grammatically possible?

a The suggestion went down well.
b The suggestion was gone down well.
c The suggestion went down well with my boss.
d The suggestion didn't go down well.

→ Now check your answers in the key.

Practise

1 **Fill in the gaps in these sentences using the correct form of** *go down.*

a How do you think the suggestion will _____ with your teacher?
b The news of the move _____ extremely badly with his wife.
c Her speech didn't _____ well with the audience.

2 **Imagine that you are in the following situations, and write a sentence saying how your family would react to this news. Use a form of** *go down* **and an adverb in your answers.**

a You've got a new job.
   This would _____.
b You've been arrested by the police.
   This would _____.
c You've won a competition.
   This would _____.

→ Now check your answers in the key.

Build your vocabulary

IDIOMS

go down like a lead balloon (=people do not like something):
- *My joke* **went down like a lead balloon.**

go down a storm/treat (=people like something very much):
- *The movie* **went down a storm** *at the awards ceremony.*

SYNONYMS

In American English, **go over** can be used with the same meaning:
- *The news of her promotion* **went over** *well with her colleagues.*

40 go down (2)

Study Read these sentences carefully.
- ▸ There was a storm and all the computers **went down**.
- ▸ The website **went down** for two hours because of a problem with the software.
- ▸ The system is **going down** in ten minutes.
- ▸ Always save your work in case the computer **goes down**.

Check Use the sentences in the Study box to help you do these exercises.

MEANING

If a computer, a server, etc. *goes down*, what happens?

a It stops working temporarily.
b It falls off the desk.
c It stops working permanently.

GRAMMAR

Which of these are grammatically possible?

a The computer went down.
b The computer was gone down.
c The computer had gone down.

→ Now check your answers in the key.

Practise

1 Complete the following sentences by choosing the correct form of *go down*.

a The network _____ for two hours this morning.
  (gone down/went down/go down)

b I always save my work to disk in case my hard drive _____.
  (goes down/go down/had gone down)

c The computers _____ so no one could send any emails.
  (go down/had gone down/has gone down)

d How will we cope if the Internet _____?
  (has gone down/went down/goes down)

e We always warn clients when a server _____ for maintenance.
  (is going down/had gone down/go down)

2 Answer the following questions, using the verb *go down*.

a Why didn't you send me an email?
  Because _____.

b Why didn't you give the teacher your homework?
  Because _____.

→ Now check your answers in the key.

Build your vocabulary

SYNONYMS

To **crash**:
  ▸ *Files can be lost if the system suddenly* **crashes**.

SIMILAR VERBS

To **fall over** is often used with a similar meaning:
  ▸ *We need a system that will not keep* **falling over**.

41 go in for something

Study Read these sentences carefully.

▸ He doesn't **go in for** really bright colours.
▸ I didn't know you **went in for** dancing. You never told me!
▸ I've never really **gone in for** that sort of thing, but then I thought, why not try it?
▸ You didn't **go in for** sports at school, did you?
▸ This isn't the sort of book I would usually **go in for**.

Check Use the sentences in the Study box to help you do these exercises.

MEANING

Choose the right phrase in *italics* to
make true sentences about *go in for*.

a **Go in for** means to do or use
something *often/rarely* because you
like/don't like it.
b **Go in for** is most often used in
positive/negative sentences.

GRAMMAR

Which of these are grammatically
possible?

a What sports do you go in?
b I don't usually go in for thrillers.
c My friend goes in for tell these awful
jokes.
d What sports do you go in for?
e I don't go usually in for thrillers.

→ Now check your answers in the key.

Practise

1 Match the two halves of these dialogues.

a You're not eating. Aren't you hungry?
b So what sort of music do you guys go
in for?
c What did you think of her new
boyfriend? I don't think he's really
her type.
d You don't really go in for going to
concerts, do you?

i No, not really. I prefer to listen to
stuff on CDs.
ii Well, it's just that I don't really go in
for spicy food.
iii I know, she doesn't usually go in for
smart guys in suits!
iv House, techno and drum and bass,
normally.

2 Rewrite these sentences using a form of *go in for* in each.

a What sort of music did you like when you were a teenager?
What sort of music _____?

b He's always been really interested in going to places that tourists don't visit.
He's always _____.

c She's not really into wearing lots of make-up.
She doesn't _____.

d I've never been fond of wearing black clothes.
I've _____.

→ Now check your answers in the key.

Build your vocabulary

OTHER MEANINGS If you **go in for** a kind of work (for example law or advertising),
you choose it as a career:

▸ *After his exams, he wants to **go in for** marketing.*
▸ *I should **have gone in for** medicine, like my father.*

42 go into something

- The report **goes into** the question of work-life balance.
- She said she needed an operation, but didn't **go into** any details.
- I asked him why he left his job, but he wouldn't **go into** it.
- I'm not **going into** why Frank was fired.
- She's not coming, for reasons which I won't **go into**.

Check Use the sentences in the Study box to help you do these exercises.

MEANING

Which two of these verbs are closest to this meaning of *go into something*?

a to examine
b to enter
c to discuss
d to tell

GRAMMAR

Which of the following are grammatically possible?

a He didn't go into details about the accident.
b He didn't go into it.
c He didn't go into how the accident happened.
d Details were not gone into.

→ Now check your answers in the key.

Practise

1 Which question goes with each response?

a The author goes into that later in the book.
b It's private. I don't want to go into it now.
c I don't know. He didn't go into details.
d We'll go into the question of cost later.
e You don't have to go into that if you don't want to.

i When did he realize his computer had been stolen?
ii Will the building work be very expensive?
iii How did the main character's mother die?
iv What if he asks me about how I got the money?
v Why are you and Ben not talking to each other?

2 Complete the following sentences, using a form of *go into something* and one of the words or phrases below.

it   details   how it started   what's involved   what causes stress

a You can't talk about stress without _____.
b I've had a big row with my boyfriend, but I don't want _____.
c He said there was a fire but didn't _____.
d If you're interested in the job, come to my office and I'll _____

_____.

e He mentioned that he used to be in the army, but didn't _____

_____.

→ Now check your answers in the key.

Build your vocabulary

SIMILAR VERBS   → LOOK INTO SOMETHING

43 go through something

Study Read these sentences carefully.

▶ The team has been **going through** a bad patch and desperately needs to win.
▶ Her parents **went through** a messy divorce last year.
▶ It was a terrible experience and I hope I never have to **go through** it again.
▶ You should speak to a sympathetic person who understands what you're **going through**.

Check Use the sentences in the Study box to help you do these exercises.

MEANING

Choose the two words which best complete this meaning of *go through something*.

difficult   happy   interesting
unpleasant   tiring

to experience a _____ or
_____ time or event

GRAMMAR

Which of these are grammatically possible?

a He went through a divorce.
b He went it through last year.
c He went through it last year.
d A divorce was gone through by him.

→ Now check your answers in the key.

Practise

1 Respond to these statements using a form of *go through* in each answer and the phrase in brackets.

a Teenage sons! Jack's behaviour is terrible!
Don't worry, he's just _____. (difficult phase)
b She's still depressed after her friend's death.
Everyone _____. (a grieving process)
c He's had a terrible time over the last few months.
It's difficult to imagine _____. (what)
d How's your business doing?
We _____ *last year, but sales are improving now*. (financial difficulties)
e I'm ready to move on with my life now.
That's good. You've _____ *in recent years*. (a lot)

2 Think of a difficult situation you have been in. Write one or two sentences about it, using forms of *go through*.

_____
_____

→ Now check your answers in the key.

Build your vocabulary

SYNONYMS

The verb **undergo** is more formal:
▶ *She **underwent** a major operation on her heart.*

44 go through with something

Study Read these sentences carefully.
- ▸ He didn't have the courage to **go through with** his plans.
- ▸ They **went through with** the wedding even though the bride was very ill.
- ▸ He says he'll take us to court, but he won't **go through with** it.

Check Use the sentences in the Study box to help you do these exercises.

MEANING

Which of these explanations best fits the meaning of *go through with something*?

a to refuse to do something which has been planned

b to go somewhere in order to do something

c to do something that you have planned or promised to do, even if it is difficult

GRAMMAR

Which of these are grammatically possible?

a I can't go through with the operation.

b I can't go through with it.

c I couldn't go through with the operation.

d The operation was gone through with.

→ Now check your answers in the key.

Practise

1 **Add the correct form of *go through with* to complete these sentences.**

   a She was determined to _____ it.

   b The company unwisely _____ the merger against all advice.

   c I know I could never _____ an operation like that.

   d They are _____ plans to build new offices.

2 **You have received this email from a friend. Underline the <u>two</u> sentences which show whether your friend has decided to do something, and then rewrite them using a form of *go through with*.**

   _____

   _____

   _____

   _____

   _____

	Hello — Inbox	
Delete Junk	Reply Reply All Forward	Print

From: Maya
Subject: Hello!
   Date: 12 June 2009 12:22:08 GMT
     To: anna@free-mail.net

Hi Anna, How are you? Things have been very busy here. I have applied for a new job and have got an interview next week. I'm not sure I really want the job now, but it would be stupid not to do the interview, I think. Do you remember I told you we had some plans drawn for a new bathroom? Well, we have finally decided to do it, and building work starts next week so I'm expecting lots of mess! Hope to hear your news. Love Maya

→ Now check your answers in the key.

45 grow out of something

Study Read these sentences carefully.

- Children **grow out of** their clothes very quickly.
- Most children **grow out of** early speech problems.
- Owen is going through a very difficult phase at the moment, but he'll **grow out of** it.
- He wanted to be a racing driver when he was young — something that he never **grew out of**!

Check Use the sentences in the Study box to help you do these exercises.

MEANING

1 If a child *grows out of* a coat, what happens?

a They try the coat to see if it fits.
b They become too big to wear the coat.
c They tear the coat because they are too big for it.

2 If a child *grows out of* a type of behaviour or an illness, what happens?

a They gradually stop doing it or having it as they get older.
b They start to do it or have it as they get older.

GRAMMAR

Which of these are grammatically possible?

a He grew out of his shoes.
b He'll grow out of them.
c His shoes grew out of him.
d He was grown out of them.

→ Now check your answers in the key.

Practise

Rewrite the following sentences so that the meaning stays the same, using a form of *grow out of something*.

a Hay fever is an illness that people often stop suffering from as they get older.

Hay fever _____.

b I used to bite my nails but now I'm older I don't.

I _____.

c This skirt is too small for me.

_____.

d At what age did you stop suffering from asthma?

When _____?

e Analysts hope that these are problems the country will soon overcome.

Analysts hope that _____.

→ Now check your answers in the key.

Build your vocabulary

SYNONYMS

The verb **outgrow** means the same as *grow out of*:

- *She's already **outgrown** her school uniform.*
- *He's **outgrown** his tantrums, thankfully.*

OPPOSITES

You can **grow into** clothes:

- *The coat's too big for her now, but she'll **grow into** it.*

46 keep on; keep on doing something

Study Read these sentences carefully.

▸ It's still raining! If it **keeps on** like this, I'll go crazy!
▸ After 15 km I was exhausted, but I just **kept on**.
▸ I've failed my driving test again, but I'm going to **keep on** taking it until I pass.
▸ He **kept on** getting lost, so he decided it was time to buy a map.
▸ Don't **keep on** complaining about your job — you're lucky to have one.

Check Use the sentences in the Study box to help you do these exercises.

MEANING

Choose the correct phrases to complete this meaning of *keep on*.

If you **keep on** doing something, you *continue/stop* doing it and *do not stop/do not continue*.

GRAMMAR

Only <u>one</u> of these sentences is correct. Which one? Correct the mistakes in the others.

a Why do you keep on going there?
b Why is he keeping on doing that?
c He keeps himself on getting into trouble.
d Trying was kept on by me.

→ Now check your answers in the key.

Practise

1 In the following sentences, the speakers are showing how they feel by using *keep on doing something*. Which attitude do you think each has?

determination   frustration   admiration   support

a He's so wonderful. He *keeps on buying* me flowers and taking me to restaurants. He's the man of my dreams! _____

b My daughter *keeps on asking* me for money. I wish she'd get a job! _____

c I'm going to *keep on learning* these phrasal verbs. _____

d Don't worry, *keep on applying*. I'm sure you'll get a job soon. _____

2 What might you say in these situations?

a You are telling a friend how your neighbours annoy you by playing loud music every night.

_____

b You are explaining to somebody in the garage that your car regularly makes a horrible noise.

_____

c You are complaining that nobody can ever spell your name correctly.

_____

→ Now check your answers in the key.

Build your vocabulary

SYNONYMS   **carry on, carry on doing something**:
▸ If it **carries on** raining, I'll go crazy!

See also **go on, go on doing something** in *Really Learn 100 Phrasal Verbs*.

47 keep somebody **on**

Study Read these sentences carefully.

- ▸ We are hoping to **keep on** all our staff with no redundancies.
- ▸ What is the firm's policy on **keeping** employees **on** beyond retiring age?
- ▸ They gave her a job when she was 18 and **kept** her **on** until she retired at 65.
- ▸ He was not fired, but was given a formal written warning and **kept on**.

Check Use the sentences in the Study box to help you do these exercises.

MEANING

1 Who can *keep somebody on*?

  a A company can keep on its workers.
  b A worker can keep on their company.

2 If you are *kept on*, what do you do?

  a You start working for a different firm.
  b You continue working for the same firm.

GRAMMAR

Which of these are grammatically possible?

  a He was kept in on the same job for years.
  b He was kept on in the same job for years.
  c They couldn't keep on me.
  d I'll be kept on indefinitely.
  e I'll be kept indefinitely on.

→ Now check your answers in the key.

Practise

1 Find and correct <u>one</u> mistake in each of the following sentences.

  a Most employees in the state sector are keep on until they reach retirement age.
  b My uncle worked for a firm, but they couldn't afford keep him on, and he was made redundant.
  c I hope they'll keep on me for as long as I want to work there.
  d It's a temporary job just for the summer, so they won't keep everybody who starts working in July but only has a short temporary contract on.

2 Answer these questions in any way you like, using a form of *keep somebody on* in each answer.

  a In your country, how old are men and women usually when they retire?

  _____

  _____

  b Is it possible to be *kept on* and start a new job at the same time? If so, how?

  _____

  _____

→ Now check your answers in the key.

Build your vocabulary

SIMILAR VERBS

Take somebody on means 'to employ somebody':
  ▸ *A number of businesses are now **taking on** new staff.*

OPPOSITES

Lay somebody off is used when you stop employing somebody because there is not enough work for them to do:
  ▸ *If we lose the contract, we will have to **lay** some staff **off**.*

48 let somebody off; let somebody off something

Study Read these sentences carefully.

▸ The meeting isn't so important. I'll **let** you **off** this time.
▸ The bus driver **let** him **off** the fare because he didn't have any money.
▸ I promised to help with the job and she's not going to **let** me **off** it.
▸ She was **let off** doing her homework because she'd been sick.

Check Use the sentences in the Study box to help you do these exercises.

MEANING

If you *let somebody off something,*
what do you do?

a You allow somebody to do what
they want.
b You allow somebody to help you.
c You allow somebody not to do
something.

GRAMMAR

There is a grammatical mistake in
one of the following sentences. Find
it and correct it.

a He let her off because she was
tired.
b He let her off the job.
c He let it off her.
d He let her off it.
e She was let off the job.

→ Now check your answers in the key.

Practise

1 **Match the two halves to make complete sentences or comments.**

a I'd love you to come tomorrow, but
b They didn't let him off the bill, but
c As a reward for their good behaviour
d Everyone has to do the assignment.

i he can pay a little each month.
ii I can't let you off.
iii I'll let you off if you're busy.
iv the kids were let off doing their
chores.

2 **Rewrite the sentences below using a form of *let somebody off (something)*, so that
the meaning stays the same.**

a I said he didn't need to pay me back if he didn't have any money.

_____

b I asked my manager if I could miss the meeting.

_____

c If you're tired, I don't mind if you don't come with me.

_____

→ Now check your answers in the key.

Build your vocabulary

IDIOMS

let somebody off the hook (= to allow somebody to avoid
something difficult or unpleasant):
▸ *He's found somebody else to help him, which **lets me off the hook**.*

OTHER MEANINGS Another important meaning of **let somebody off (with
something)** is 'to punish somebody lightly or not at all':
▸ *The judge **let** the driver **off** very lightly **with** a small fine.*
▸ *He kicked the other player! I can't believe the referee **let** him **off**.*

49 live on something

Study Read these sentences carefully.
- He's paid so well that he and his family can easily **live on** his salary.
- Across the globe, 1 person in 5 **lives on** less than $1 a day.
- I don't earn enough to **live on**.
- Pensions are so small these days that it's often difficult for people to **live on** them.

Check Use the sentences in the Study box to help you do these exercises.

MEANING

Which one of these is the correct meaning of *live on something*?

a to have a particular amount of money for all the things you need
b to be alive for long enough to spend all your money on something
c to have a job which brings enough money for the things you need

GRAMMAR

Which of these are grammatically possible?

a This isn't enough to live on.
b This isn't enough to live on it.
c I don't know how they can live on their wages.
d This isn't enough on which to live on.

→ Now check your answers in the key.

Practise

1 Complete each sentence with **one** word from the box and the correct form of *live on*.

| salary | pension | benefits | royalties | wages | income | allowance |

a My wife and I are both working, and our combined _____ is enough

_____ .

b I can hardly _____ my _____ — I only get £5.25 an hour.

c You need to save for your retirement, in case your _____ is not

sufficient _____ .

2 Look carefully at these sentences. They are all correct, and all contain the words 'live' and 'on'. But only *two* of them have the phrasal verb *live on*. Which two?

a She lived on her own for about six years.
b My job only just gives me enough to live on.
c They have lived on this street all their lives.
d I find I can live quite comfortably on what I earn now.

→ Now check your answers in the key.

Build your vocabulary

OTHER MEANINGS   **Live on something** also means 'to eat one particular kind of food very often':
- *When I was a student, I **lived on** bread and cheese.*

SIMILAR VERBS   **Live off something**:
- *It's quite hard to **live off** what I earn.*

Live off somebody has a negative meaning, and shows that you think somebody is relying on another person for money to live:
- *You can't **live off** your parents forever — when are you going to find a job?*

50 look into something

Check Use the sentences in the Study box to help you do these exercises.

MEANING	GRAMMAR
Which of these verbs means the same as *look into*?	**Which of these are grammatically possible?**
a to see	**a** We'll look into the matter.
b to try	**b** We'll look into it.
c to investigate	**c** We looked the matter into.
	d We looked it into the matter.
	e The matter was looked into.

→ Now check your answers in the key.

Practise

1 Choose the correct form of the verb to fill the gaps in these sentences. You will not need to use all of them.

look into it   are looking into   is looking into   look into   looks into   looked into

a Police _____ the possibility that the crimes are linked.

b I will _____ as a matter of urgency.

c A committee was appointed to _____ the case.

d We _____ buying a new computer but decided against it.

e The government _____ ways of encouraging people to recycle.

2 You are the manager of a restaurant. You have received this letter complaining about a meal. Write a short reply, using the verb *look into something*.

_____

_____

_____

_____

_____

> 52 Lockwood Road
> London E
> 27 May 200
>
> Dear Sir/Madam
>
> I am writing to complain about a meal we had at your restaurant last week. The food which was served was not cooked properly, and when we complained to the waitress, she was very rude and refused to take the food back. I asked to speak to the manager, and was told that you were not available. I would be grateful if you could give this matter some urgent attention.
>
> Yours faithfully
>
> Duncan Smith

→ Now check your answers in the key.

Build your vocabulary

SIMILAR VERBS   → GO INTO SOMETHING

REVIEW

Forming New Phrasal Verbs

New phrasal verbs are appearing in the language all the time, especially in the areas of computers and technology, business, and everyday informal English.

Exercise 1 – Computers

Can you match a verb on the left with a particle on the right to make a phrasal verb connected with using a computer?

a time   down/up
b mouse   through
c click   out
d page   over

Now match each verb with a definition:

e to move the mouse so that you point to a particular area on the screen
f to move forwards/backwards in a computer document or web page
g to go beyond a particular time limit and stop working or be no longer valid
h to visit a website by clicking on a link or advertisement on another web page

Exercise 2 – Business

Match the phrasal verbs in these sentences with the meanings in the box.

> draw attention to   lead   introduce   increase

a Demonstrators are trying to **flag up** the problem of animal cruelty.
b The new service is to be **rolled out** next year.
c Some insurance companies have **ramped up** their prices over the last few years.
d The President will **head up** a delegation which is to visit Europe next spring.

Exercise 3 – Informal Language

Choose the correct definition for these informal phrasal verbs.

a We **maxed out** both our credit cards shopping in New York.
   ☐ to reach the limit of something   ☐ to be at the beginning of something

b Being in this empty house at night really **creeps** me **out**!
   ☐ to make somebody feel safe   ☐ to make somebody feel frightened

c I was **blissing out** over my chocolate fudge cake.
   ☐ to feel very annoyed   ☐ to feel very happy

d What a beautiful day! You really **lucked out** with the weather.
   ☐ to be lucky   ☐ to be unlucky

Exercise 4

Have you noticed that new phrasal verbs don't have to come from verbs? How many new phrasal verbs on this page have been formed using a particle with a noun?

_____   _____
_____   _____
_____   _____

Go

In this book you have studied **go** in combination with:

down   in for   into   through   through with

Exercise 1 – Meanings

Match each verb with a definition.

go through
go in for
go down
go through with
go down well/badly
go into

a to be successful/unsuccessful or popular/unpopular
b to stop working for a period of time
c to experience a difficult or unpleasant time or event
d to examine or discuss something carefully
e to like something, or to have something as an interest or hobby
f to do something that you have planned or promised to do, even though it may be difficult or unpleasant

Exercise 2 – Synonyms

In a–d below there is a word or phrase which could be replaced by one of the phrasal verbs in Exercise 1. Underline this word or phrase and then rewrite the sentence using the phrasal verb in the correct tense.

a My presentation to the management committee went over very well. Everybody seemed interested in what I had to say.

_____

b The Senator had to be rescued from his car after its state-of-the-art on-board computer crashed, leaving the vehicle immobilized.

_____

c This month's report looks into the question of whether young people are eating a balanced, healthy diet, or if they are consuming too much junk food.

_____

d Since the accident, she has undergone major surgery on both legs and is working hard to regain full use of her right hand.

_____

Exercise 3 – Test Yourself

Complete these sentences with the correct form of a phrasal verb with go. Some verbs will need to be in the positive, and some negative.

a I'd rather _____*not go into*_____ that now. We can discuss it at the next meeting.

b It was very embarrassing. The joke _____ well and nobody laughed.

c My son has never _____ computer games.
   He'd rather be out playing sport.

d She'd planned to ask him to leave, but in the end she _____ it.

e I had a terrible day. The computers _____ and I lost all my work.

f Unless you've been in the same situation, you'll never understand what
   we _____ right now.

Take

In this book you have studied **take** in combination with:

back   down   in   out   to

Exercise 1 – Meanings

Put the correct adverb or preposition into the empty boxes
below. You can use the same one more than once. Use pages 85
to 90 to help you.

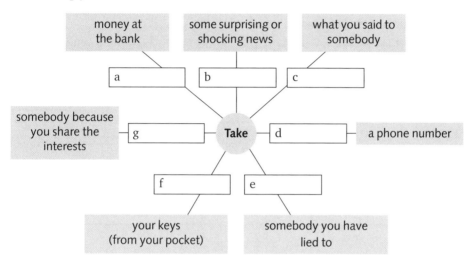

Exercise 2

Now put the adverbs and prepositions into the correct place in
these sentences, using the chart above to help you.

a   Just wait while I get a pen and I'll take _____ your address.

b   I couldn't take _____ what he was telling me. It was such a shock.

c   Many people are taken _____ by false advertising.

d   I shouldn't have said such hurtful things. I wish I could take them _____.

e   I've never really taken _____ Anna's boyfriend. He seems a bit arrogant.

f   I took _____ £100 from my account to pay for the dress.

Exercise 3 – Synonyms

The following are synonyms of <u>four</u> of these phrasal verbs with **take**.
Write a different phrasal verb next to each one.

a   write down   _____

b   deceive   _____

c   retract   _____

d   withdraw   _____

Work and Study

These phrasal verbs can all be used when you are talking about **work and study**:

back up	drop out	pick up	try out	throw out
brush up	go into	refer to	sum up	take down
come up with	keep on	set out		

Exercise 1 – Meanings

Decide which of the phrasal verbs in the list above are most useful for each of these areas:

Learning skills or subjects	Trying, staying in or leaving a job or a course of study	Discussing, writing or thinking about something

Exercise 2

Choose the best way to complete these sentences.

a If you don't start doing some work at college, …

☐ they'll *keep* you *on* .   ☐ they'll *drop* you *out*.   ☐ they'll *throw* you *out*.

b The company is having to get rid of some staff. I really hope they …

☐ *keep* me *on*.   ☐ *back* me *up*.   ☐ *refer to* me.

c Have you never worked with spreadsheets before? Don't worry, you'll …

☐ *brush* it *up* easily.   ☐ *pick* it *up* easily.   ☐ *sum* it *up* easily.

d I want to impress my boss. I need to …

☐ *look into* a good idea.   ☐ *sum up* a good idea.   ☐ *come up with* a good idea.

e I hope the quality of teaching improves. Otherwise I'm afraid students will …

☐ *drop out*.   ☐ *throw out*.   ☐ *pick up*.

f He got a place on the Work Trial Scheme, and a local garage offered to …

☐ *refer to* him.   ☐ *try* him *out*.   ☐ *set* him *out*.

g She worked hard and achieved everything she …

☐ *set out* to do.   ☐ *tried out* to do.   ☐ *kept on* to do.

Exercise 3

Here are some tips on how to write an essay.
Use a phrasal verb from the list at the top page R4 to fill each gap.

> **Essay Writing Tips**
>
> Make sure you are well prepared by attending any necessary lectures and doing some background reading. You will find it helpful to take notes, as you will then have something to _____ when you come to write the essay.
>
> At the beginning of the essay, state clearly the points that you _____ to prove so that the reader knows what to expect, and don't forget to always _____ your arguments with supporting evidence.
>
> Always _____ the main points of your essay in the final paragraph, and don't forget to check through your work before you hand it in!

Exercise 4 – Test Yourself

Test your knowledge of these verbs by completing the sentences with a suitable phrasal verb in the correct tense, and any other words you need.

a I must _____ my French before we go to France.

b She _____ the course because she wasn't enjoying it.

c Young children _____ languages very quickly.

d The report _____ the impact of climate change on the economy.

e We hope to be able to _____ 40% of the workforce.

f Our shareholders won't like this. We're going to have to _____ an alternative.

g If you want to register for the course, I need to _____ your name, address and telephone number.

h You know lots of Japanese words now. You can _____ when you get to Tokyo.

i He deliberately _____ to turn the boss against me and get me _____!

j I've got an idea I'd like to _____ on you.

k The figures I _____ in my presentation applied to last year's sales.

l He didn't have time to read the report so he asked me to _____ for him.

Exercise 5

Choose three of the phrasal verbs at the top of the page, and use them to write sentences which are true for you, for example:

I **tried out** a few different jobs before I became a nurse.

_____

_____

_____

How People Behave

Dealing with Problems

Exercise 1 – Meanings

Look at the verbs in the box below and put them in the correct column according to their meaning. You can look back at the main pages to help you.

calm down; calm sb/sth/yourself down
clear up; clear sth up
face up to sb/sth
get over sth
mix sth up
come up against sb/sth
fall for sth
mess sth/sb up; mess up

Meeting Problems	Making Problems	Solving Problems

Exercise 2

Complete these sentences with one of the verbs in Exercise 1 in the correct form.

a After this injury, Mike has to _____ the fact that his career in football is over.

b The announcer was terrible. She kept getting all the names _____.

c I would wait until she has _____ before you mention the matter again.

d It was a really simple job. I don't know how you _____ so badly.

e When they tried to open a new supermarket, they _____ a lot of opposition.

Relationships

Exercise 3 – When things go wrong

Complete the email with one of these phrasal verbs in the correct form, and any other words you need.

break off
put down
take back
fall out

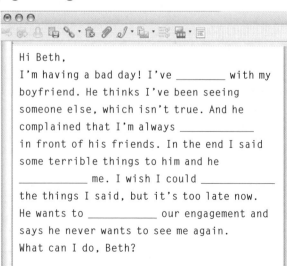

Hi Beth,
I'm having a bad day! I've _____ with my boyfriend. He thinks I've been seeing someone else, which isn't true. And he complained that I'm always _____ in front of his friends. In the end I said some terrible things to him and he _____ me. I wish I could _____ the things I said, but it's too late now. He wants to _____ our engagement and says he never wants to see me again. What can I do, Beth?

Exercise 4

Now match each verb with its definition:

a break sth off
b walk out on sb
c fall out with sb
d put sb down
e take sth back

i   to have an argument with somebody
ii   to criticize somebody and make them feel stupid
iii to leave somebody you have a close relationship with
iv   to admit that something you said was wrong
v   to end something suddenly

Exercise 5 – Getting on with people

Complete the questionnaire with the correct particles.
You can look back at the main pages to help you.

Will you be a good boss?
Try our simple questionnaire!

1 If one of your team keeps asking for more interesting work to do, do you **give** ____ **to** her
   a always?
   b sometimes?
   c never?

2 One of your team argues with you a lot in meetings. Would you **put** him ____?
   a yes
   b perhaps
   c never

3 A new colleague has trouble **fitting** ____. Would you:
   a tell him/her to try harder?
   b ask somebody in the team to help him/her?

4 A junior member of your team **shows** ____ a lot, telling colleagues that he is better than them. Would you:
   a quietly tell him the truth?
   b give him work to do which you know he will do badly?
   c **put it** ____ **to** youth and inexperience and say nothing?

5 Your team tell you that their coffee machine has broken. There is no money to buy a new one. Do you:
   a pay for a new one yourself?
   b tell them they will have to **do** ____ coffee?
   c **make** ____ **for** it by allowing them extra time to go out for coffee?

Exercise 6

Now use some of the verbs from Exercise 5
to say what you think a good manager should be like.

A good manager should never _____ .

A good manager always _____ .

_____

Common Particles

In this book you have studied verbs combining with many particles, including:

down   out   over   up   on

Exercise 1

You may be able to see some patterns of meaning in the verbs you have studied. Write each of the verbs in the box below in the correct column according to the meaning of the particle. Look back at the main pages to help you.

stand up for	bring down
take out	brush up

Improving	**Supporting**

Reducing	**Removing/ Leaving**

Exercise 2

Circle the correct particle.

a Sam never did any work, and in the end he was thrown _____ of college.
  off   out   over

b Why do you always put me _____?
  You never praise or encourage me.
  up   down   in

c Do you have any evidence to back _____ these claims?
  out   over   up

d OK, everybody, calm _____! Nothing bad going to happen.
  down   off   up

e I can't believe he just walked _____ on he after all those years together.
  off   over   out

f An apology won't make _____ for the way you've behaved.
  off   up   over

g All this arguing is really getting me _____
  down   out   over

h There's been a lot of confusion and we nee to clear things _____ .
  off   out   up

Now add verbs a–h into the columns in Exercise 1.

Exercise 3

Read the sentences and then circle the word that most closely matches the meaning of the particle in each pair.

a ● What time will you be arriving? I'll *look out for* you.
  ● What does it say? I can't quite *make it out*.
  removing   observing   choosing

b ● I spent ages organizing my files, and somebody's *messed* them all *up* again!
  ● She *tore up* the letter in disgust.
  collecting   damaging   stopping

c ● I'll be glad when these exams *are over* – then we can enjoy ourselves.
  ● Let's go first and *get* this *over* with as quickly as possible.
  finishing   covering   communicating

d ● How long do you think the company will *keep* you *on*?
  ● Can you *pass* this message *on* to your colleagues please?
  encouraging   starting   continuing

Test Yourself

Use these two pages to test yourself on a variety of the verbs
that you have studied in this book.

Exercise 1

Read this account of a prison breakout, and then choose
one of the words or phrases below to fill each gap.

Two criminals broke a_____
Birmingham Prison early this morning,
and they are still on the run. Robert Bohol,
one of the police officers b_____
the incident, gave the following statement:

'The two men had been complaining of
severe stomach pains. We now know that
they were not ill, but unfortunately prison
staff c_____ for their story,
believing that the men had d_____
a virus or some other illness. On their way
to a nearby hospital in an ambulance, the
men somehow managed to escape when
the vehicle stopped at traffic lights.

To be honest, the story doesn't
add e_____ . How can prison
staff f_____ so easily? One or more
prison employees must have helped the
men, and we are doing everything we can to
g_____ this mystery up.'

A fellow prisoner has told reporters that
he knew about the plan. 'I thought it was
a crazy idea, but they were determined
to h_____ it. I can't believe
they i_____ it off.'

Police say that the men are not dangerous,
but that the public should j_____
anybody behaving suspiciously.

a in	into	out	out of
b looked into	looking into	go into	gone into
c fell	took	made	were
d gone down	come up	picked up	eaten up
e in	up	off	along
f take in	have taken in	have been taken in	were taken in
g add	brush	blow	clear
h go through with	come up with	come up against	do away with
i did	pulled	broke	called
j stand up for	make up for	fall for	look out for

Exercise 2

Match each phrasal verb on the left with
a suitable object on the right.

a wrap up
b stick to
c run into
d do away with
e fit in with
f make up for

i   something you don't need
ii   a birthday present
iii lost time
iv   your diet
v   the rest of the team
vi   an old friend

Which of these phrases can
be used to talk about:

g doing things now that you
   couldn't or didn't before?
h a chance meeting?
i continuing to do something?
j being comfortable in a group
   of people?

Exercise 3

Rewrite the sentences using the word in **bold** so that the meaning stays the same. Use 2-5 words in each gap.

a After the power cut, there wasn't any electricity for 2 days in our house.   **do**
   After the power cut, we had to _____ for 2 days.

b He's quite depressed at the moment because of his problems with money.   **getting**
   His money _____ down at the moment.

c I'm busy all morning, but I've got time to see you this afternoon at 2.30 p.m. **fit**
   I can _____ this afternoon at 2.30 p.m.

d We had to cancel the party because of the bad weather.   **off**
   Because of the bad weather, the party had _____.

e You can stay at my house if you want. There's plenty of room.   **put**
   There's plenty of room at my house. I can _____.

f That jacket used to fit him perfectly, but he's too big for it now.   **grown**
   He _____ that jacket.

Exercise 4

Which of these sentences are correct? Write ✗ or ✓ next to each one.

a ☐ The exam consists of two parts.
  ☐ The exam consists two parts of.

b ☐ If I'm ever in trouble, can I count on you to help?
  ☐ If I'm ever in trouble, can I count you on to help?

c ☐ That letter's important. Don't tear up it!
  ☐ That letter's important. Don't tear it up!

d ☐ That shirt looks too small. Why don't you try on a bigger size?
  ☐ That shirt looks too small. Why don't you try a bigger size on?

e ☐ The words 'rob' and 'steal' are very similar. I always mix up them.
  ☐ The words 'rob' and 'steal' are very similar. I always mix them up.

f ☐ If the system doesn't work, we should do away with it.
  ☐ If the system doesn't work, we should do it away with.

g ☐ That book isn't yours, Ellie! Put back it, please.
  ☐ That book isn't yours, Ellie! Put it back, please.

Exercise 5

Which of the verbs in Exercise 4 allow you to separate the verb and the particle? Write them into the correct box according to whether the verb is inseparable (e.g. *consists of*), or separable (e.g. *tear up*).

verb + preposition	verb + adverb
consist of	*tear up*

ANSWER KEY

Forming New Phrasal Verbs

EXERCISE 1

a time out
b mouse over
c click through
d page down/up
e mouse over
f page down/up
g time out
h click through

EXERCISE 2

a draw attention to
b introduce
c increase
d lead

EXERCISE 3

a to reach the limit of something
b to make somebody feel frightened
c to feel very happy
d to be lucky

EXERCISE 4

time out
mouse over
page down/up
flag up
ramp up

head up
max (i.e. 'maximum') out
bliss out
luck out

NOTE **Time** and **head** are also used as verbs (*to time sb/sth; to head sth*)

Go

EXERCISE 1

a go down well/badly
b go down
c go through
d go into
e go in for
f go through with

EXERCISE 2

a went over very well
   My presentation…went down very well…
b crashed
   …its on-board computer went down…
c looks into
   This month's report goes into the question…
d has undergone
   …she has gone through major surgery…

EXERCISE 3

b did not go down
c gone in for
d didn't/couldn't go through with it
e went down
f are going through

Take

EXERCISE 1

a take out
b take in
c take back
d take down
e take in somebody
f take out
g take to somebody

EXERCISE 2

a down   c in   e to
b in   d back   f out

EXERCISE 3

a take sth down
b take sb in
c take sth back
d take sth out

Work and Study

EXERCISE 1

Learning skills or subjects
brush up   pick up

Trying, staying in or leaving a job or a course of study
drop out   throw out
keep on   try out

Discussing, writing or thinking about something
back up   set out
come up   sum up
go into   take down
refer to

EXERCISE 2

a they'll throw you out
b keep me on
c pick it up easily
d come up with a good idea
e drop out
f try him out
g set out to do

EXERCISE 3

… have something to refer to …
… the points that you set out to …
… always back up your arguments …
Always sum up the main points …

EXERCISE 4

a brush up (on)
b dropped out of
c pick up
d goes into
e keep on
f come up with
g take down
h try them out
i set out,
   thrown out
j try out
k referred to
l sum it up

How People Behave

EXERCISE 1

Meeting Problems
come up against sb/sth
face up to sb/sth
fall for sth

Making Problems
mess sth/sb up; mess up
mix sth up

Solving Problems
calm down; calm sb/sth/yourself down
clear up; clear sth up
get over sth

EXERCISE 2

a face up to	d messed (it) up
b mixed up	e messed (it) up
c calmed down	f came up against

EXERCISE 3

I've fallen out with …
… putting him down in front of …
… he walked out on me.
I wish I could take back …
… break off our engagement.

EXERCISE 4

a v	c i	e iv
b iii	d ii	

EXERCISE 5

1 in	4 off, down
2 down	5 without, up
3 in	

Common Particles

EXERCISE 1

Improving
brush sth up	make up for sth
clear sth up	

Supporting
back sth up	stand up for sb

Reducing
bring sth down	get sb down
calm sb down	put sb down

Removing/Leaving
take sth out	walk out on sb
throw sb out	

EXERCISE 2

a out	c up	e out	g down
b down	d down	f up	h up

EXERCISE 3

a observing		c finishing
b damaging		d continuing

Test Yourself

EXERCISE 1

a out of	f have been taken in
b looking into	g clear
c fell	h go through with
d picked up	i pulled
e up	j look out for

EXERCISE 2

a ii	c vi	e v
b iv	d i	f iii

g make up for lost time
h run into an old friend
i stick to your diet
j fit in with the rest of the team

EXERCISE 3

a … we had to do without electricity …
b His money problems are getting him down …
c I can fit you in …
e … the party had to be called off.
f I can put you up.
g He has grown out of …

EXERCISE 4

a ✓		c ✗		e ✗		g ✗	
✗		✓		✓		✓	
b ✓		d ✓		f ✓			
✗		✓		✗			

EXERCISE 5

Verb + preposition
consist of sth	do away with sth
count on sb	

Verb + adverb
tear sth up	mix sth up
try sth on	put sth back

51 look out for somebody or something

Study Read these sentences carefully.
- ▸ It's always worth **looking out for** broken glass if you're on the beach with bare feet.
- ▸ Security staff are trained to **look out for** anyone who is behaving strangely.
- ▸ I'm always **looking out for** special offers in the supermarket.
- ▸ Pete should be coming tonight. I've been **looking out for** him.
- ▸ **Look out for** 'Lord of the Rings' — it's a brilliant movie and you really should see it.

Check Use the sentences in the Study box to help you do these exercises.

MEANING
Are the following sentences true or false?

a People often **look out for** somebody or something that might be dangerous.

_____

b If you **look out for** somebody, you are trying to find or meet them.

_____

c If you **look out for** something, you examine it carefully.

_____

GRAMMAR
Find and correct any mistakes in the following.

a Look out for thieves.
b I'll be looking you out for.
c This is a book to look out — you'd really enjoy it.
d This is a book to look out for — you'd really enjoy it.
e That book was being looked out for by me, but I couldn't find it.

→ Now check your answers in the key.

Practise

Look for or look out for? **Choose the correct verb.**

a Drivers must always *look for/look out for* other road users.
b Excuse me, I'm *looking for/looking out for* the train station. Is it near here?
c Wherever you are, it's essential to *look for/look out for* pickpockets.
d 'Katie has just moved into a house on your street!' 'Really? I'll *look for/look out for* her.'
e I anxiously *looked for/looked out for* my name on the team lists.

→ Now check your answers in the key.

Build your vocabulary

RELATED WORDS
A **lookout** is a place where somebody watches from, to see if there is any danger.

To **be on the lookout for** something or somebody means to watch carefully in order to find something or somebody, or to be prepared for any problems:
- ▸ *We're always **on the lookout for** new markets.*

SIMILAR VERBS
Look out! is used on its own to tell somebody to be careful.

See also **look for somebody or something** in *Really Learn 100 Phrasal Verbs*.

OTHER MEANINGS
To **look out for somebody** also means 'to take care of somebody and make sure that nothing bad happens to them':
- ▸ *My brother and I always **looked out for** each other at school.*

52 make something out

Study Read these sentences carefully.

- ▸ She could just **make out** a dark figure by the door.
- ▸ The photo is too dark to **make** the faces **out**.
- ▸ He's written something else at the end, but I can't **make** it **out**.
- ▸ I can hear voices. Can you **make out** what they're saying?
- ▸ I can't **make out** why he's marrying somebody like her.

Check Use the sentences in the Study box to help you do these exercises.

MEANING

If you can *make something out,*
which of these might you be able
to do? More than one answer is
correct.

a see something
b understand something
c say something
d hear something

GRAMMAR

Which of these are
grammatically possible?

a I could just make it out.
b I could just make out it.
c I could just make the shape
   out.
d I could just make out the
   shape.
e It was just made out.

→ Now check your answers in the key.

Practise

1 Replace the <u>underlined</u> words with an appropriate form of *make out*.

a She gradually <u>saw</u> somebody walking towards her in the fog.
b I couldn't <u>hear</u> what he was saying.
c It all happened so fast, he couldn't <u>understand</u> what was going on.

2 Make up answers to these questions using a form of *make something out*.

a What could you see in the dark?

_____

b Can you see anything without your glasses?

_____

c What do you think of Jake?

_____

d How well do you understand Japanese now?

_____

→ Now check your answers in the key.

Build your vocabulary

IDIOMS

A very common phrase is **as far as I can make out**:
- ▸ *As far as I can make out, he's telling the truth.*
- ▸ *The photos were about 10 years old, as far as she could make out.*

SIMILAR VERBS

To **make out (that)…** means 'to claim that something is true that
may not be':
- ▸ *She made out that she was earning a fortune.*

53 make up for something; make up for doing something

Study Read these sentences carefully.

- We **made up for** lost sales by increasing prices.
- I didn't sleep well last night, so I'm going to **make up for** it tonight and go to bed early.
- How are you going to **make up for** what you said to me yesterday?
- She bought him a special present to **make up for** forgetting his birthday.
- The service was awful, but this was **made up for** by the excellent food.

Check Use the sentences in the Study box to help you do these exercises.

MEANING

Choose the correct words in *italics* to make true sentences about *make up for*.

a **Make up for** something means to do something *good/bad* to balance the effects of something *good/bad*.

b If somebody or something **makes up for** something, the situation becomes *better/worse*.

GRAMMAR

Which of these are grammatically possible?

a This doesn't make up for.
b This doesn't make up for my mistakes.
c You've got a lot to make up for.
d This doesn't make up for it.
e This doesn't make it up for.
f Extra costs were made up for by record sales.

→ Now check your answers in the key.

Practise

1 Make sentences by joining a phrase on the left with a suitable one from the box on the right, using a form of *make up for*.

a I didn't eat much during the day, but I _____

b The airline gave us all a free meal at the airport as a way of _____

c We've had to increase our prices to _____

i having such poor results in the last financial year.

ii it by having a huge supper.

iii the flight being delayed.

2 Rewrite the part of the sentence in *italics* without changing the meaning, using a suitable form of *make up for* and any other words you need.

a The firm have paid me some money *to compensate for overcharging me*.

_____

b The apartment is very small, *but it's got a lovely garden, which I really like*.

_____

→ Now check your answers in the key.

Build your vocabulary

SYNONYMS

To **compensate (for something)** is more formal:
- *Nothing can **compensate for** the death of a loved one.*

54 **mess** something or somebody **up**; **mess up**

Study Read these sentences carefully.

- You've **messed up** my life! I wish I'd never met you!
- Drugs can **mess** people **up** and completely destroy their lives.
- What have you done to the settings on my computer? You've **messed** it all **up**, and I can't get it to work.
- The arrangements **got messed up**; everyone arrived late, and it was a disaster.
- It's your last chance. Don't **mess up**, or you'll be in big trouble.

Check Use the sentences in the Study box to help you do these exercises.

MEANING

Are the following sentences about the meaning of this verb true (T) or false (F)?

a If you **mess up**, you make a big mistake.

_____

b If you **mess up**, you are in an untidy place. _____

c If you **mess somebody up**, they look very untidy. _____

d **Mess up** has a negative meaning.

_____

GRAMMAR

There is a mistake in two of these sentences. Find and correct them.

a I've really messed up it this time.

b The experience messed him up for the rest of his life.

c I can't believe you've messed it up again.

d He had been completely messed by prison.

→ Now check your answers in the key.

Practise

1 Correct one mistake (of grammar or spelling) in each sentence.

a I don't know how could you mess up something so simple!
b It's the kind of thing it would be so easy to messing up.
c Did you do well or did you messed up?

2 Read the following extract from Bob's diary. Write sentences about Bob's day using forms of *mess up* or *mess something up*. There are some clues to help you.

Oh dear, what a morning! First of all, breakfast went wrong, because I let the milk boil over and then I burnt the toast. Then I got to work half an hour late. My boss told me I had an important meeting in my office with Mr Umar at 11. I waited and waited but nobody came. At 12 Mr Umar phoned and said he was in his office waiting for me, and I think he was annoyed. It turned out that my boss had told me the wrong thing! Let's hope tomorrow's better!

(breakfast) _____

(his boss) _____

→ Now check your answers in the key.

Build your vocabulary

RELATED WORDS ADJECTIVE: ˌmessed-ˈup

- He's just a **messed-up** kid.

55 mix somebody or something up

Study Read these sentences carefully.

▶ Young children often **mix up** 'b' and 'd'.
▶ The waiter had **mixed** our orders **up** and we got the wrong food.
▶ I'm always **mixing** her **up** with her sister.
▶ Present simple and present continuous tenses are often **mixed up**.

Check Use the sentences in the Study box to help you do these exercises.

MEANING

Choose the best explanation of
this meaning of *mix somebody or
something up*.

a to change the position of somebody
   or something
b to put something in the wrong place
c to confuse people or things by
   thinking that one person or thing is
   another

GRAMMAR

Which of these are grammatically
possible?

a I mixed them up.
b I mixed their names up.
c I mixed up their names.
d I mixed up them.
e They were mixed up.

→ Now check your answers in the key.

Practise

1 Complete these sentences using an appropriate form of *mix somebody or
   something up* and any other words you need.

   a I look like my brother and people often _____.

   b The words are very similar. Be careful not to _____.

   c The travel agent _____ our booking with somebody else's so we
      didn't receive our tickets.

   d How could you possibly have _____ her daughter?

2 Now use *mix somebody or something up* to write two sentences about things that
   you sometimes confuse.

   _____

   _____

→ Now check your answers in the key.

Build your vocabulary

IDIOMS

To **get A and B mixed up** and to **get A mixed up with B** are very
common phrases:
▶ *I always **get** 'net' and 'gross' **mixed up**.*
▶ *I think you've **got** me **mixed up with** my brother.*

SYNONYMS

Confuse somebody or something (with somebody or something)
and **mistake somebody or something for somebody or something**
can be used in more formal language. **Muddle somebody or
something up** is informal:
▶ *People often **confuse** me and/with my twin sister.*
▶ *These tablets can easily **be mistaken for** sweets.*

56 mix something up

Study Read these sentences carefully.

▸ We **mixed up** the tracks in the forest and got completely lost.
▸ Is that the postman that **mixes** all my mail **up** with yours?
▸ I'd sorted all those papers out and now you've **mixed** them **up** again!
▸ The details were all **mixed up** in his mind.

Check Use the sentences in the Study box to help you do these exercises.

MEANING

If somebody *mixes things up*, do they:

a arrange them in a better way?
b make them confused or untidy?
c think one thing is another?

GRAMMAR

Correct the mistakes in these sentences. There is <u>one</u> in each.

a She's mixed all up the papers.
b The letters mixed up.
c She mixed up them.
d She mixed the letters on the desk.

→ Now check your answers in the key.

Practise

1 Complete these sentences, using a form of *mix something up* and any other words you need.

a I'm trying to find some books by a particular author, but they _____ _____ on the shelves.
b I can't find my clean clothes! They _____.
c Before he started to fit the jigsaw pieces together, he _____ _____.
d All our shoes are in a horrible mess! Who _____?
e I dropped my file on the way home and now all my notes _____ _____.

2 Use the verb *mix something up* to describe a situation when some of your things have become confused or untidy.

_____

_____

→ Now check your answers in the key.

Build your vocabulary

RELATED WORDS

NOUN: **'mix-up** (This is a countable noun meaning 'a mistake that causes confusion' or 'a situation when there is confusion'):
▸ *There was a **mix-up** over my ticket and I couldn't fly home.*

ADJECTIVE: **,mixed 'up**
▸ *My papers are all **mixed up**.*
▸ *I'm sorting out my **mixed-up** papers.*
▸ *I'm all **mixed up** (= confused).*

SYNONYMS

To **muddle something up** (especially in British English):
▸ *Somebody has **muddled up** all the application forms.*

57 pass something on

Study Read these sentences carefully.
- ▶ He had been accused of **passing on** state secrets.
- ▶ Could you **pass** this message **on** to John?
- ▶ If you know anyone who might be interested in this magazine, please **pass** it **on**.
- ▶ The virus can be **passed on** by close contact.
- ▶ The increase in gas prices will be **passed on** to consumers.

Check Use the sentences in the Study box to help you do these exercises.

MEANING

Which of these verbs best completes this meaning of *pass something on*?

say   give   throw

to _____ something to somebody else

GRAMMAR

Which of these are grammatically possible?

a I'll pass the message on.
b I'll pass on the message.
c I'll pass the message on James.
d I'll pass it on to James.
e The message was passed on.

→ Now check your answers in the key.

Practise

1 Choose the correct form of *pass something on* to fill the gaps in these sentences.

be passed on   pass on   is passed on   been passed on

a The gene for colour-blindness _____ from the mother.
b Colds are very infectious and can easily _____ .
c The rise in production costs has _____ to customers.
d Could you _____ this information to your colleagues?

2 Rewrite the following sentences so that the meaning stays the same, using a form of *pass something on*.

a Please give this leaflet to anyone who might be interested.

_____

b He got the gene for red hair from his father.

_____

c I got chickenpox and gave it to both my brothers.

_____

→ Now check your answers in the key.

Build your vocabulary

SIMILAR VERBS

hand something on:
- ▶ *Please **hand** the book **on** to somebody else when you have finished with it.*

58 pick something or somebody out

Study Read these sentences carefully.

▶ We're having difficulty **picking out** a name for the baby.
▶ Do you like the necklace? I **picked** it **out** for you myself.
▶ If I asked you for your favourite movie, which one would you **pick out**?
▶ The brightest students **were picked out** for special training.
▶ The accused **was picked out** in an identity parade and will stand trial next week.

Check Use the sentences in the Study box to help you do these exercises.

MEANING

Which three of these words can mean the same as *pick out*?

a to select
b to identify
c to remove
d to choose
e to reject
f to pick up

GRAMMAR

Which of the following are grammatically possible?

a I picked immediately it out.
b They weren't sure which one to pick it out.
c I knew you'd pick that one out.
d She'll be able to pick him out easily.
e This is picked out by the majority of customers.

→ Now check your answers in the key.

Practise

1 In these sentences, circle both words in the verb, and underline the object.

a Picking out the best fruits to buy isn't always easy.
b I usually pick the freshest out.
c How did you pick me out from all the other faces in the picture?
d Speed cameras on roads can pick out drivers who are going too fast and photograph them.

2 Complete the sentences with the correct form of *pick out* and a pronoun if necessary.

a He's so tall that you can easily _____ in a crowd.

b None of the menu was in English, so I didn't know what _____ .

c I heard that the police have _____ two main suspects, but they're still questioning other people.

d It's hard _____ one reason for the failure.

e It's an amazing island and I'm having trouble _____ one place where you should go.

→ Now check your answers in the key.

Build your vocabulary

SYNONYMS

To **choose**; to **select** is more formal:
▶ *The customer **selected** the most expensive suit in the store.*

To **identify** can be used when you recognize somebody or something in a group:
▶ *She could not **identify** her attacker from the photos.*

59 pick something up (1)

Study Read these sentences carefully.

▸ If you live in the USA, you'll **pick up** the language easily.
▸ I **picked** this tip **up** by watching golf on TV.
▸ I know lots of search tips for the Internet. I **picked** them **up** from my kids!
▸ A lot of my recipe ideas were **picked up** when I was eating in restaurants.

Check Use the sentences in the Study box to help you do these exercises.

MEANING

If you *pick something up*, do you learn it:

a by studying it very hard?
b and then forget it soon afterwards?
c without trying very hard?

GRAMMAR

Which of these are grammatically possible?

a I'm picking up a bit of Turkish.
b I picked some ideas up.
c He picked up it easily.
d Their tips picked up on the radio.

→ Now check your answers in the key.

Practise

1 Match the two halves to make complete sentences.

a It's a fashion idea I picked up
b I picked up the phrase
c I picked up my quick route to the airport
d I picked this cocktail recipe up
e The kids picked up an American accent

i after hearing it on a radio advert.
ii after having one in a bar in Cuba.
iii when we were staying in Chicago.
iv by looking at what people were wearing in Italy.
v from a map in a guide book.

2 Rewrite the following so that the meaning stays the same, using a form of *pick up*.

a You can discover a lot of information about a country by reading the newspapers.
   You _____.
b I've learned so many tips by watching my daughter's tennis lessons.
   I _____.
c He finds loads of facts just by surfing the Internet.
   He _____.
d Jana learnt Japanese very quickly when she was in Japan.
   Jana _____.
e Even experienced drivers get bad habits over the years.
   Even experienced drivers _____.

→ Now check your answers in the key.

Build your vocabulary

SIMILAR VERBS   Look at **pick somebody or something up** in *Really Learn 100 Phrasal Verbs*.

60 pick something up (2)

Study Read these sentences carefully.

▶ I must have **picked up** this virus on my recent trip.
▶ My computer seems to have **picked** a bug **up** from somewhere.
▶ 'Are those new shoes?' 'Yes, I **picked** them **up** in the sales.'
▶ Up in the mountains you can't **pick up** a good phone signal.
▶ Many diseases are **picked up** by people travelling.

Check Use the sentences in the Study box to help you do these exercises.

MEANING

Which choice a - d means the same as the sentence below?

Where did you pick it up?

a Where did you start it?
b Where did you learn it?
c Where did you get it?
d Where did you ask for it?

GRAMMAR

Which of these are grammatically possible?

a She has picked up a nasty bug.
b I picked it up at the pool.
c They picked up it on holiday.
d The disease picked up twenty people.

→ Now check your answers in the key.

Practise

1 Complete the following with the correct form of *pick up* and one of the objects below. Use each object only once.

the disease   it   €40   a signal   the channel   the accent

a She had a skin problem and she didn't know where she _____.
b I _____ in tips last night.
c We can't watch RTV because we can't _____ here.
d I _____ when I was at school in America, because everyone spoke like that.
e Sorry it took so long to phone you — I couldn't _____.
f Often people _____ by touching infected animals.

2 What sport are the people talking about in the sentences? Choose one of the options below. Use each option once only.

swimming   football   snooker

a He can't play on Saturday because he's picked up an ankle injury.
b I picked a wrist injury up in practice and so I can't play.
c I've picked up a skin infection and I can't do it for three weeks.

→ Now check your answers in the key.

Build your vocabulary

SYNONYMS

Catch something also means to 'get a disease', especially illnesses like flu or a cold:
▶ He **caught** a cold when walking in the hills.

Detect something can be used for picking up a phone or TV signal.

61 point somebody or something out

Study Read these sentences carefully.

▸ He drove us round the town, **pointing out** the interesting buildings.
▸ Can you **point** his house **out**, because I can't see it?
▸ If you want to meet Rob, I'll **point** him **out** to you when he arrives.
▸ The stolen car was **pointed out** to the police.

Check Use the sentences in the Study box to help you do these exercises.

MEANING

Which of the following means the same as *point something out*?

a to talk about something for the first time
b to show which thing you are referring to
c to show something to the police

GRAMMAR

One of these sentences has a grammatical mistake. Find it and correct it.

a He pointed out our hotel.
b Can you point it out to me because I can't see it?
c It was easy to see after she pointed out it.
d The two new students were pointed out by their teacher.

→ Now check your answers in the key.

Practise

1 Match the two halves to make complete sentences.

a When we get to the party I'll
b The mountain had
c I didn't notice the fire until my neighbour
d The first aid position was

i been pointed out to us already.
ii pointed out by a lifeguard.
iii point John out to you.
iv pointed it out to me.

2 Complete the answers to the questions, using an appropriate form of *point out* and any other words you need.

a Where can I find the local museum?

   The tourist information office can _____ for you.

b Where can I find the photo files on the computer?

   They _____ yesterday!

c Do you know which person here is Gabriele?

   No, but Yvain knows her. If you ask him, he'll _____ .

d Where is the statue of Napoleon?

   _____ to you. Look, it's over there.

→ Now check your answers in the key.

Build your vocabulary

OTHER MEANINGS **Point something out** also means 'to mention something in order to give somebody information about it or make them notice it':

▸ *I **pointed out** several mistakes in his report.*
▸ *I must **point out** that my part in the rescue was very small.*

62 pull something off

Study Read these sentences carefully.

▶ The Socialist Party managed to **pull off** a surprise victory in the election.
▶ You got the deal? I can't believe you really **pulled** it **off**!
▶ The Chicago Bulls **pulled off** an amazing win.
▶ I need to get 75% in the exam. I don't know if I **pulled** that **off** or not.
▶ If anyone can **pull it off**, you can.

Check Use the sentences in the Study box to help you do these exercises.

MEANING

Choose the right phrases to explain
this meaning of *pull something off*:

to *succeed in doing/fail to do*
something which is *easy/difficult*

GRAMMAR

Which of the following are
grammatically possible?

a I pulled off.
b I pulled it off.
c I pulled off it.
d I pulled off a great win.

→ Now check your answers in the key.

Practise

1 Complete the sentences with the right form of *pull off* and a pronoun where
necessary.

a Once again, she's succeeded in _____ a magnificent result.

b Nobody thought they would be able _____.

c He can always _____ a great performance if he really needs to.

d Yesterday Manchester United _____ their tenth win of the
season to go into first place.

e Everybody agreed that he had managed _____ the best speech
of his career.

f It was a daring raid and they very nearly _____.

2 Have you ever managed to *pull off* something that you were proud of? Write one
or two sentences, using a form of *pull something off* where you can.

_____

_____

→ Now check your answers in the key.

Build your vocabulary

SYNONYMS

bring something off:
▶ *He's famous for **bringing off**/**pulling off** the biggest bank
robbery in history.*

63 **pull through**; **pull through** something

Check Use the sentences in the Study box to help you do these exercises.

MEANING

Which <u>two</u> of the following
are closest to the meaning
of *pull through, pull through
something*?

a to move
b to deal with
c to recover from
d to manage

GRAMMAR

Which of these are grammatically
possible?

a He pulled through.
b He pulled through the operation.
c He pulled the operation through.
d He pulled it through.
e He pulled through it.
f The operation was pulled
through.

→ Now check your answers in the key.

Practise

Rewrite these sentences using a form of *pull through* in each.

a The doctors do not know if he will get better.
   The doctors _____.
b We're all praying that she gets well.
   We _____.
c The kids had a terrible time, but they are beginning to recover from their ordeal.
   The kids _____.
d The company is borrowing more money to help it survive the market downturn.
   The company _____.

→ Now check your answers in the key.

Build your vocabulary

SIMILAR VERBS

Get better is a more general way of saying that somebody **pulls
through** an illness or injury, either serious or not:
▸ *I hope you **get better** soon.*
▸ *My wrist is **getting better**.*

Recover means the same as **get better**, but is more formal and is
only used about people:
▸ *He's still **recovering from** his operation.*

Survive (something) can be used to refer to dealing with a
difficult situation:
▸ *The business was close to bankruptcy but it **survived**.*

64 put something back

- 'It's too good to wear', he said, **putting** the watch **back** in the box.
- She gently **put** the baby **back** in the crib.
- You can borrow my books, but please **put** them **back** afterwards.
- The cream will **put back** the moisture your skin has lost in the sun.
- She gets irritated if things **aren't put back** in the right place after being used.

Check Use the sentences in the Study box to help you do these exercises.

MEANING

Choose the right phrase to make true sentences about *put back*.

a If you **put something back**, you put it *where it was before/in a new place*.

b **Put something back** is *always/often/never* followed by a phrase that says 'where'.

c The object of **put back** is usually *a thing/a person*.

GRAMMAR

Find and correct any mistakes in the following.

a I forgot to put the book back.
b Please put it back.
c Could you please put back it?
d Please put back the book.
e I put immediately it back.
f It still hasn't been put back in the right place.

→ Now check your answers in the key.

Practise

1 Choose the correct underlined phrase to complete the sentences.

a It isn't yours — you should <u>put it back</u>/<u>take it back</u> where you found it.
b I need to <u>put my books back</u>/<u>take my books back</u> to the library.
c I've broken one of my aunt's plates. She's furious, so I think I should <u>replace it</u>/<u>put it back</u>.
d Remember to put it back <u>to where you found it</u>/<u>where you found it</u>.

2 Complete the sentences in an appropriate way with a form of *put back*, a suitable object (a noun or pronoun) and any other words you need.

a He's the worst roommate I've ever had. He never _____.
b If you want your CDs to last a long time, _____.
c I'm really sorry, but I forgot to _____.
d Can you remember to _____ in the fridge?

→ Now check your answers in the key.

Build your vocabulary

SYNONYMS

To **replace something** is more formal:
- She **replaced** the book on the shelf.

OPPOSITES

To **leave something lying around**. This has a negative meaning, and suggests that somebody is untidy:
- Why do you have to **leave** all your clothes **lying around**?

65 put somebody or yourself down

Study Read these sentences carefully.

- My last boss was very critical and was always **putting** people **down**.
- Some TV interviewers love to **put down** politicians who don't answer their questions.
- Why does he **put** me **down** and make me look stupid in front of the whole class?
- 'I was awful.' 'Oh come on, don't **put** yourself **down**, you did fine.'
- I hate being **put down** like that — I can never think of what to say back to her.

Check Use the sentences in the Study box to help you do these exercises.

MEANING

Choose the right word to complete this meaning of *put somebody down*:

to say something *kind/unkind* to somebody, and make them feel *good/bad*, especially when there *are/aren't* other people listening.

GRAMMAR

Which of these are grammatically possible?

a He's quick to put himself down.
b He puts down anyone who criticizes him.
c I hate the way he puts down her all the time.
d Why are you putting me down?
e I'm tired of being put down.

→ Now check your answers in the key.

Practise

1 Match the two halves to make complete sentences.

a I just can't stand
b I don't know why they
c She sometimes
d I wish you wouldn't keep
e Sometimes it's very tempting

i putting me down like that.
ii being put down in front of my colleagues.
iii to just put him down and shut him up.
iv puts people down without really meaning to.
v put him down like that — he was only asking!

2 Describe a situation where you felt you had been 'put down' by somebody. Try to use a form of *put down* in your answer.

_____

_____

→ Now check your answers in the key.

Build your vocabulary

RELATED WORDS

NOUN: **a 'put-down.** This is a countable noun meaning 'a remark or an action that is intended to make somebody look stupid':
- *Most people don't really know how to respond to **put-downs** and just get embarrassed.*

SIMILAR VERBS

Look at **put somebody or something down** in *Really Learn 100 Phrasal Verbs*.

66 put something down to something

Study Read these sentences carefully.
- He **puts** his success **down to** hard work.
- They didn't do a lot of work and the boss **put** it **down to** tiredness.
- The crime rate is rising. What do you **put** this **down to**?
- I'm very bad at remembering names. I **put** it **down to** getting older!
- The accident was **put down to** bad luck.

Check Use the sentences in the Study box to help you do these exercises.

MEANING

Choose two of the words below to complete this meaning of *put something down to something* using the words below:

explain   deny   stopped   caused

to _____ that an event

is _____ by something

GRAMMAR

Which of these are grammatically possible?

a You can't put the defeat down to stupidity!

b We put it down to boredom.

c I am putting down to him the bad news.

d The result was put down to his hard work.

→ Now check your answers in the key.

Practise

1 Complete these sentences with one of the verb forms (gerunds) below. You will not need to use them all.

lying   being   changing   playing   working

a Urs was exhausted. He put it down to _____ all night.

b Nobody would believe him. I put it down to his _____ to everyone last year.

c Maria is very good at racket sports. She puts it down to _____ tennis for years as a child.

d He didn't say anything at the meeting. I put it down to him _____ tired.

2 Look at the sentences below. What do you think the people are talking about?

a I put it down to him smoking and drinking too much.

_____

b I put it down to nerves.

_____

→ Now check your answers in the key.

Build your vocabulary

SIMILAR VERBS   **Chalk something up to something** is more informal:
- *I thought something terrible had happened to you! You can **chalk** it **up to** my vivid imagination.*

Attribute something to something is more formal:
- *They **attributed** his discovery **to** his careful research.*

67 put somebody out

Study Read these sentences carefully.

▸ I didn't want to **put** my aunt **out**, so I only stayed one night with her.
▸ I'd love a cup of coffee, if it doesn't **put** you **out** too much.
▸ Would it **put** your friends **out** if we brought the kids with us?
▸ I hope I'm not **putting** you **out** by leaving so early.

Check Use the sentences in the Study box to help you do these exercises.

MEANING

Which of the following is the best explanation of this meaning of *put somebody out*?

a to make somebody leave a place or a job
b to make trouble, problems or extra work for somebody
c to make somebody angry or annoyed

GRAMMAR

Which of these are grammatically possible?

a She hated putting her family out.
b She hated putting out her family.
c She hated putting them out.
d She hated putting out them.
e She hated putting it out.

→ Now check your answers in the key.

Practise

1 **Decide whether somebody or something has *put* the speaker *out* or not, according to what he/she says.**

a I'm going to the store anyway, so it's no trouble to get your shopping.
b He stayed with us for three months, which was rather difficult.
c This is the third time I've done this trip today!
d They had to totally reorganize the event when they discovered that she wasn't coming.

2 **Complete each sentence with a form of *put out* and a noun or pronoun.**

a I hope our arriving late didn't _____ at all.
b Would it _____ too much if he came to stay for a day or two?
c Could I talk to you for a moment, if it isn't _____?
d Can you call us when you get there, if it _____ too much?

→ Now check your answers in the key.

Build your vocabulary

OTHER MEANINGS   **Put yourself out**, meaning 'to make a special effort to do something for somebody', is also common:

▸ She really **put herself out** for her visitors.

In the passive, **be put out** usually means 'be upset or offended':

▸ He **was** extremely **put out** when I couldn't remember his name.

SIMILAR VERBS   Look at **put something out** in *Really Learn 100 Phrasal Verbs*.

68 put somebody up

Study Read these sentences carefully.

- ▸ She **puts up** foreign students in the summer.
- ▸ Alice is **putting** my parents **up** because my apartment is too small.
- ▸ If you need a place to stay, I could **put** you **up** in my spare room.
- ▸ Our flight was cancelled and we **were put up** in a hotel for the night.

Check Use the sentences in the Study box to help you do these exercises.

MEANING

Which two of the definitions below best explain this meaning of *put somebody up*?

a to move somebody to a higher position
b to arrange for somebody to stay somewhere
c to let somebody stay in your home
d to stay in somebody's home

GRAMMAR

Which of these are grammatically possible?

a I put his parents up.
b I put up his parents.
c I put them up.
d I put up them.
e They were put up in a hotel.

→ Now check your answers in the key.

Practise

1 Complete the following in an appropriate way, using a form of *put somebody up* in each and any other words you need.

a He's got nowhere to stay. Will you _____ ?
b My sister usually _____ when I go back home to Edinburgh.
c They _____ by the company her father worked for.
d There's no room for you to stay here — I'm already _____ .

2 Write a suitable response to the following sentences, using a form of *put somebody up* and any other words you need in each.

a Where will you stay when you go to France?
   My brother _____ .
b I can't afford to stay in a hotel.
   I know somebody _____ .
c There are a lot of people travelling from Ireland for our wedding.
   How will you _____ ?
d What happened to the people who couldn't go back to their homes after the hurricane?
   They were _____ .

→ Now check your answers in the key.

Build your vocabulary

SIMILAR VERBS   **Take somebody in** means to allow somebody to stay in your home, sometimes for money:
- ▸ *She **takes in** paying guests.*
- ▸ *When his parents died, his uncle **took him in** and brought him up.*

69 refer to somebody or something

Study Read these sentences carefully.

- She never **refers to** her accident.
- I think I know which photos you are **referring to**.
- I wasn't sure who he was **referring to**.
- He **referred to** her as 'my best friend'.
- The subject is **referred to** in Chapter 3.

Check Use the sentences in the Study box to help you do these exercises.

MEANING

Which of these explanations best fits this meaning of *refer to*?

a to mention or speak about somebody or something
b to read a book
c to look at somebody or something

GRAMMAR

Which of these are grammatically possible?

a I won't refer to the matter again.
b I won't refer it to again.
c I won't refer to it again.
d It was never referred to again.

→ Now check your answers in the key.

Practise

1 Match the two halves to make complete sentences.

a The victims were not
b Her mother never
c You know who
d She is always
e Why are ships

i I am referring to.
ii referred to him again.
iii referred to as 'she'?
iv referred to by name.
v referring to him as 'that nice man'.

2 Complete these sentences in an appropriate way, using a form of *refer to* in each and any other words you need.

a My mother saw what happened but _____.

b I'm not sure _____.

→ Now check your answers in the key.

Build your vocabulary

OTHER MEANINGS **Refer to** can also mean 'to look at something for information':

- *Please **refer to** chapter 5 for more details.*
- *It is important to provide a record that can **be referred to**.*

It is also used to show that something is connected with something:

- *The term 'visually handicapped' **refers to** students with serious difficulties in seeing.*

70 remind somebody **of** somebody or something

> **Study** Read these sentences carefully.
> - Kirsty **reminds** me **of** my sister in many ways.
> - Nora **reminded** Anna **of** her mother.
> - The scene **reminded** her **of** a Japanese painting.
> - I only saw Raj once, but John **reminds** me **of** him very much.
> - Looking at his serious face and big round glasses, I **was reminded of** an owl.

Check Use the sentences in the Study box to help you do these exercises.

MEANING

Choose the best explanation of this meaning of *remind somebody of somebody or something*.

a to make you think of another person, place, etc. because they are similar
b to tell somebody that they should do something
c to try to remember somebody or something

GRAMMAR

There is a grammatical mistake in one of the following sentences. Find it and correct it.

a She reminds me of my mother.
b She reminded me of my mother.
c She is reminding me of my mother.
d She reminded me of her in many ways.

→ Now check your answers in the key.

Practise

1 Rewrite the following sentences so that the meaning stays the same, using a form of *remind somebody of*.

a She makes me think of a horrible teacher I once had.

_____

b I thought the town was very like Vevey in Switzerland.

_____

c That photograph always makes me think of our trip to Florida.

_____

d The smell of bread baking took me back to my childhood.

_____

2 Think of two people or things you know that are similar in some way, and write a sentence about them using a form of *remind somebody of*.

_____

→ Now check your answers in the key.

Build your vocabulary

SYNONYMS

Bring somebody or something to mind and **take somebody back (to something)** have similar meanings but are more formal:
- *His style **brings to mind** one of my other favourite writers.*
- *That song **takes me back to** my student days.*

SIMILAR VERBS

If you **remind** somebody about/of something, you help them remember it:
- *Can you **remind** me about the meeting this afternoon? I'm sure I'll forget.*

71 run into somebody

- I couldn't believe it when I **ran into** Pete in Paris. I hadn't seen him for years.
- Hello! I didn't expect to **run into** you here!
- Being a teacher, I'm always **running into** my old students.
- You'll never guess who I **ran into** today.

Check Use the sentences in the Study box to help you do these exercises.

MEANING	GRAMMAR
In the example *I ran into Pete*, which of these statements are true?	Which of these are grammatically possible?
a I was running.	a I ran into Ben the other day.
b I met Pete.	b I'm always running into Ben.
c We had arranged to meet.	c I ran him into the other day.
d I didn't know Pete would be there.	d I ran into him the other day.
e Pete got hurt.	

→ Now check your answers in the key.

Practise

1 **Read the extract from a diary and decide which people in the list below the writer *ran into*. Write Yes or No beside each.**

> Over breakfast, my wife and I talked about where we wanted to go for our next trip. On the way to work I was surprised to meet Bob, my old friend from school. I hadn't seen him for years! Anyway, he said he'd been to Hong Kong and it was fabulous. At work, I asked if anyone had been there. Bill and Barbara said they had, but didn't think it was the most interesting place in the world. Met Dave for lunch as usual. I couldn't believe it — the waitress who served us was an old neighbour of mine from the days when I was a student. I think her name was Angela, but I couldn't really remember. Got back home to hear voices in the kitchen — my wife was talking to Joanna. I'd forgotten we had invited her for supper, but we had lots of food in the freezer, so it was no problem.

a his wife	c Bill and Barbara	e Angela
b Bob	d Dave	f Joanna

2 **Each sentence contains <u>one</u> grammatical mistake. Find and correct it.**

  a Hello! I didn't think I would ran into you here!
  b In this job, you always running into strange people.
  c Who did you say did you run into yesterday?

→ Now check your answers in the key.

Build your vocabulary

SIMILAR VERBS   Look at **come across somebody or something** in *Really Learn 100 Phrasal Verbs*.

OTHER MEANINGS   **Run into** can also mean to 'start to have difficulties or problems':
                  ▶ *The project **ran into** problems right from the start.*

72 see to somebody or something

Study Read these sentences carefully.
- ▸ She was outside **seeing to** the animals.
- ▸ I've got the children to **see to**.
- ▸ Don't worry about washing the dishes. I'll **see to** it.
- ▸ You should get your bad back **seen to**.
- ▸ He **saw to** it that she got all the help she needed.

Check Use the sentences in the Study box to help you do these exercises.

MEANING

If you *see to somebody or something*, what do you do?

a You go and look at somebody or something.
b You find somebody or something.
c You deal with something or somebody.

GRAMMAR

There is a grammatical mistake in two of these sentences. Find and correct them.

a I'll see to the children.
b I'll see it to.
c I'll see to it.
d I'll get it seen to.
e I'll see to that she gets help.

→ Now check your answers in the key.

Practise

1 **Match the two halves to make complete sentences.**

a I've got no time
b She has her own affairs
c I must get back and
d With all this rain, it's a good thing
e I'll see to it personally

i to see to.
ii we got the roof seen to.
iii to stop and see to him.
iv that your complaint is investigated.
v see to the kids.

2 **Here is a list of things that need to be arranged for a trip. Choose which one you will do and write a sentence using *see to*. Then write another sentence asking your friend to do one of the other jobs.**

flights   maps   medical requirements   packing   taxi to the airport

a _____

b _____

→ Now check your answers in the key.

Build your vocabulary

SYNONYMS

Attend to means the same as **see to** but is more formal:
- ▸ *I have some urgent business to **attend to**.*
- ▸ *Can you entertain Sam while I **attend to** the baby?*

73 set out

Study Read these sentences carefully.

▸ She had achieved everything she had **set out** to do.
▸ I'm sure John didn't deliberately **set out** to upset you.
▸ The book **sets out** to make grammar easier and more enjoyable for students.
▸ It isn't as if we were **setting out** to mislead anybody.

Check Use the sentences in the Study box to help you do these exercises.

MEANING

Which of these verbs is closest in meaning to *set out*?

a to promise
b to like
c to intend

GRAMMAR

Which of these are grammatically possible?

a I did everything I set out to do.
b I didn't do everything I set out to do.
c I did everything I was set out to do.
d I did everything I set it out to do.

→ Now check your answers in the key.

Practise

1 Match the two halves to make complete sentences.

a I didn't set out
b He's a very determined runner
c Ann succeeded in
d The court was told that Stokes

i what she set out to do.
ii to cause trouble.
iii had set out to steal from the store.
iv who set out to break the world record.

2 Answer these questions using a form of *set out*, the words in brackets and any other words you need.

a What does the test aim to do?

_____ (assess, ability)

b Why did you open the business?

_____ (money)

c What was your purpose in writing the book?

_____ (best-seller)

d What did you want to prove?

_____ (results, wrong)

→ Now check your answers in the key.

Build your vocabulary

OTHER MEANINGS   To **set out** can also mean 'to leave a place and begin a journey':
▸ We **set out** at dawn.
This verb is in *Really Learn 100 Phrasal Verbs*.

74 set something out

- The report **sets out** guidelines for teachers.
- He **set** the proposals **out** clearly in a document.
- She made several points and had **set** them **out** very well.
- The terms and conditions will be **set out** fully in the contract.

Check Use the sentences in the Study box to help you do these exercises.

MEANING

Choose the explanation that best fits this meaning of *set something out*.

a to arrange text in a computer document
b to give all the details of something in a clear and organized way
c to promise to do something

GRAMMAR

Which of these are grammatically possible?

a He set the plans out in a document.
b He set out them in a document.
c He set out the plans in a document.
d He set them out in a document.
e The plans are set out in the document.

→ Now check your answers in the key.

Practise

1 Choose the correct form of *set something out* to fill the gaps in the sentences.

are set out   sets out   set them out   set out   sets out   setting out

a The minister wrote a letter _____ clearly the government's position on the matter.
b The general principles _____ in the report.
c The document _____ eight proposals for consideration.
d If there are terms that people need to know, you should _____ clearly.
e There will be a charge in addition to the fees _____ above.
f A job description _____ how an employee fits into the company.

2 Read this job advertisement. <u>Underline</u> the verb that could be replaced by a form of *set something out*. Then rewrite the sentence using *set something out*.

> **TEACHING ASSISTANT £15 000 p.a.**
> We are looking for somebody to help children reach their full potential in the classroom. You should enjoy working with children and have previous experience of working in a school environment. If you are interested please apply by 15 September to Mrs A Winterburn, stating clearly in writing why you would like this job.

→ Now check your answers in the key.

75 show off

Study Read these sentences carefully.

- ▶ Paul was **showing off** like a child.
- ▶ Suki is always **showing off** to her friends about what a big house she lives in.
- ▶ I don't like John. He always **shows off**.
- ▶ Stop **showing off**!
- ▶ He **showed off** by saying that his father was a millionaire.

Check Use the sentences in the Study box to help you do these exercises.

MEANING

1 If somebody is *showing off*, what are they doing?

   a showing you how to do something
   b doing or saying things to try and make people admire their possessions, abilities, etc.
   c trying to get you to understand something

2 If you say that somebody is *showing off*, do you:

   a like what they are doing?
   b not like what they are doing?

→ Now check your answers in the key.

GRAMMAR

Which of these are grammatically possible?

   a Sam was showing off.
   b Sam was showing off about his new car.
   c Sam was showing off it.
   d Sam was showing off to his friends.
   e Sam was showing off at his friends.

Practise

1 Write the correct preposition in the sentences. You will not need to use them all.

to   about   for   at

   a Jo was showing off _____ how much money she earns.
   b Paul is always showing off _____ his friends.
   c Ann liked to show off _____ her sister _____ her new sports car.

2 Use the correct form of *show off* to fill the gaps in these sentences.

   a I don't like people who _____ in front of their friends.
   b He was _____ because he had won the competition.
   c She _____ for weeks after she got straight As.
   d He couldn't resist _____ and hitting the ball all over the court.

→ Now check your answers in the key.

Build your vocabulary

RELATED WORDS   NOUN: a ˈ**show-off** (= a disapproving word for a person who tries to impress people with their abilities, wealth, etc.)
    ▶ *Don't be such a **show-off**!*

76 show something or somebody off

Study Read these sentences carefully.
- He was wearing a tight T-shirt to **show off** his big muscles.
- They've gone to **show** their new baby **off** to their parents.
- Amy had a limited knowledge of Spanish but she was determined to **show** it **off**.
- He's always **showing off** how smart he is.
- His new sports car is usually **shown off** to everyone who comes.

Check Use the sentences in the Study box to help you do these exercises.

MEANING

Choose the explanation that best fits this meaning of *show off*.

a to show people somebody or something that you are proud of
b to show people somebody or something that you are worried about
c to show people somebody or something because you want them to help

GRAMMAR

There is a grammatical mistake in one of these sentences. Find it and correct it.

a Helga showed off her diamond ring.
b Helga showed it off.
c Helga showed her diamond ring off at her friends.
d Helga showed her diamond ring off.

→ Now check your answers in the key.

Practise

1 Complete the sentences with the correct form of *show something or somebody off* and one of the objects below.

new products   her suntan   skills   a new watch

a The exhibition gives companies a chance to _____.
b Rob had been shopping and proudly _____.
c Jo had just got back from Italy and was _____.
d Going to a foreign country would give him a chance to _____
his language _____.

2 Think of something that you are proud of, and write a sentence using *show something or somebody off* to say who you showed it to.

_____

→ Now check your answers in the key.

Build your vocabulary

OTHER MEANINGS   To **show somebody or something off** can also mean 'to make somebody or something look attractive or seem interesting by showing their best features':
- The music **shows** the band **off** in their best light (= very well).
- Clever lighting can **show** a room **off** to its best advantage.

SIMILAR VERBS   The verb **flaunt** means the same but is usually used to show that you disapprove of somebody. The verb **show something or somebody off** can be used when you approve or disapprove:
- He **flaunts** his wealth by wearing expensive clothes and driving around in fast cars.

77 spread something out

Check Use the sentences in the Study box to help you do these exercises.

MEANING

Use <u>one</u> from each pair of words to complete this meaning of *spread something out*.

a arrange/remove   c away from/close to
b on/from   d slightly/clearly

to _____ a group of objects
_____ a surface so that they are
_____ each other and can be seen

_____ .

GRAMMAR

Which of these are grammatically possible?

a She spread the cards out.
b She spread them out.
c She spread out the cards.
d She spread out them.
e The cards were spread out.

→ Now check your answers in the key.

Practise

1 Complete the following sentences using a form of *spread something out* and one of the objects below, if necessary.

their paintings   them   the various dishes

a She took six photos from a drawer and _____ on the table.
b They laid the table, _____ .
c The children _____ to dry.
d His clothes were _____ on the floor.

2 Write this sentence so that it has the opposite meaning, using a form of *spread yourselves out*.

Can you all move closer together so I can see you better?

_____

→ Now check your answers in the key.

Build your vocabulary

SYNONYMS   **spread something**:
                 ▸ They **spread** the seeds on the soil.

OTHER MEANINGS   **Spread something out** also means to 'unfold something and put it down on a flat surface':
                 ▸ They **spread** the blanket **out** on the grass.

                 It is often used to refer to arranging things over a period of time:
                 ▸ The cost can be **spread out** over two years.

78 stand for something

- Ladies and gentlemen, our party **stands for** real change and progress in society.
- The name has a good image and **stands for** high quality.
- Great brands aim to **stand for** something in people's minds.
- I hated him and all he **stood for.**

Check Use the sentences in the Study box to help you do these exercises.

MEANING

Choose the best phrases to complete this meaning of *stand for*:

to *argue about/support/disagree with* something; to *be a symbol of/show* something

GRAMMAR

Which of these are grammatically possible?

a We stand for democracy.
b We stand for a clean environment.
c We stand democracy for.
d A clean environment is stood for by the company.

→ Now check your answers in the key.

Practise

1 Rewrite these sentences using an appropriate form of *stand for*.

a The idea of the European Union is greater integration between countries.
The European Union _____.

b All environmental organizations are in favour of protecting the planet.
All _____.

c Nobody really knows what the new president's policies actually are.
Nobody knows what _____.

2 Can you think of one person or organization that *stands (or stood) for* the following things?

a saving the environment

_____

b fighting poverty

_____

→ Now check your answers in the key.

Build your vocabulary

OTHER MEANINGS 1. **Stand for** can also be used to explain abbreviations and acronyms:
- *In this dictionary, PHR V* **stands for** *phrasal verb.*
- *AIDS is an acronym* **standing for** *'acquired immune deficiency syndrome'.*

2. It also means 'to allow something to happen or somebody to do something':
- *She was so rude to you — you shouldn't* **stand for** *it!*
- *I won't* **stand for** *this kind of behaviour.*

79 stand out

Study Read these sentences carefully.

▸ My husband is so tall that he always **stands out** *from* the crowd.
▸ Of all the places I went to in India, the Taj Mahal **stands out** *as* the most beautiful.
▸ Only one player really **stood out** *among* the others. He was just brilliant.
▸ He **stands out** *for* his extraordinary intelligence.
▸ In those days, a man with long hair really **stood out**, and people stared at him.

Check Use the sentences in the Study box to help you do these exercises.

MEANING

Choose **three words** from the list below to complete the meaning of *stand out*.

taller   better   worse   expensive
important   few   other   no

to be much ＿＿＿＿＿＿ or more
＿＿＿＿＿＿ than ＿＿＿＿＿＿
people or things

> Now check your answers in the key.

GRAMMAR

Which of these are grammatically possible?

a He really stands out.
b He stood out from all the other boys at school.
c What makes him stand out?
d What stands him out?
e He was stood out.

Practise

1 Complete the sentences with an appropriate preposition. (There may be more than one answer.) The sentences in the Study box will help you.

a She really stands out ＿＿＿＿＿＿ her bright red hair.
b I think he is the only one who stands out ＿＿＿＿＿＿ a possible future President.
c What really stands out ＿＿＿＿＿＿ this photo is the amazing range of colours.
d He stands out ＿＿＿＿＿＿ being an exceptionally talented young musician.
e There is one candidate who stands out ＿＿＿＿＿＿ all the others.

2 How would you answer these questions? Use a form of *stand out* in your answers.

a What do you think is the most beautiful place you've ever visited?

＿＿＿＿＿＿＿＿＿＿＿＿＿＿＿＿＿＿＿＿＿＿＿＿＿＿＿＿＿＿＿＿＿＿＿＿＿

b Is there anyone in your family who seems different from the others? Why?

＿＿＿＿＿＿＿＿＿＿＿＿＿＿＿＿＿＿＿＿＿＿＿＿＿＿＿＿＿＿＿＿＿＿＿＿＿

> Now check your answers in the key.

Build your vocabulary

RELATED WORDS   NOUN: **'standout** This is a countable noun, used especially in American English to refer to a person or thing that is better or more impressive than others:
▸ *This is my list of **standouts** in this week's CD chart.*

It can also be used as an adjective:
▸ **standout** *moments in the movie*

ADJECTIVE: **out'standing**
▸ *He's an **outstanding** young actor.*

80 **stand up for** somebody, something or yourself

- ▶ She always **stood up for** her friends.
- ▶ He's always telling her what to do. She should **stand up for** herself.
- ▶ When they said your work was poor, I **stood up for** you.
- ▶ I'm just **standing up for** what I believe in.

Check Use the sentences in the Study box to help you do these exercises.

MEANING

Answer 'a', 'b', or 'neither' to these questions about this meaning of *stand up for*.

a If you **stand up for** somebody, do you a) get up or b) sit down? _____

b If you **stand up for** somebody, do you a) criticize them or b) defend them? _____

c If somebody **stands up for** you, do they a) criticize you or b) defend you? _____

GRAMMAR

Which of these are grammatically possible?

a He stood up for Sally.
b He stood up Sally.
c He stood her up for.
d He stood up for her.
e Sally was stood up for.

→ Now check your answers in the key.

Practise

1 Somebody has said that a piece of your work is poor. Which of the speakers below *stands up for* you?

a 'He only had two days to do it.'
b 'His work is always poor.'
c 'Usually his work is very good.'
d 'Maybe he needs some extra help.'

2 Complete the sentences using the correct form of *stand up for* and any other words you need.

a I can fight my own battles, thanks — I don't need _____.

b Don't just sit there and take criticism. You have to learn _____ _____.

c They said I wasn't good enough to be in the team. Why didn't _____ _____?

d When they called him a liar, I _____ and said it wasn't true.

e He felt that his wife was siding with her mother rather than _____ _____.

→ Now check your answers in the key.

Build your vocabulary

SYNONYMS   → STICK UP FOR SOMEBODY, SOMETHING OR YOURSELF

SIMILAR VERBS   → STAND UP TO SOMEBODY

81 stand up to somebody or something

Study Read these sentences carefully.
- Don't be afraid to **stand up to** your boss.
- He was criticized for not **standing up to** senior executives.
- He was a cruel leader, and people who **stood up to** him were punished.
- I admire you for **standing up to** his bullying.

Check Use the sentences in the Study box to help you do these exercises.

MEANING

Choose <u>one</u> from each pair of alternatives to give the correct meaning of *stand up to somebody or something*.

to defend your position against a *more/less* powerful person or organization that is treating you *badly/well* or *fairly/unfairly*

GRAMMAR

Which of these are grammatically possible?

a She stood up to her boss.
b She stood him up to.
c She stood up to him.
d Her boss was stood up to.

→ Now check your answers in the key.

Practise

1 Which of the following describes a situation in which somebody *stands up to somebody or something*?

a A child is behaving badly so her mother tells her off.
b A group of boys threaten a younger boy and he runs away crying.
c Your boss tries to force you to do extra work and you tell him you will not do it.

2 Complete the responses to the statements using a form of *stand up to* in your answer and any other words you need.

a He's always shouting at me and making me do all the work.

   Don't let him do it. You have to _____.

b Our boss treats new employees very unfairly.

   Maybe she's testing them to see if _____.

c An older boy used to bully me at school, until one day I hit him back.

   Sometimes bullies respect you more when _____.

→ Now check your answers in the key.

Build your vocabulary

SYNONYMS

Defy somebody is similar, but is less positive than **stand up to**:
- *I wouldn't have dared to **defy** my teachers.*
- *I'm proud of the way you **stood up to** those bullies.*

SIMILAR VERBS

Square up to somebody means 'to stand facing somebody as if you are prepared to fight or argue with them'. It is used in British English.
- *She put her hands on her hips and **squared up to** him.*

→ STAND UP FOR SOMEBODY, SOMETHING OR YOURSELF

82 stick to something

Study Read these sentences carefully.

▸ She **stuck to** her diet and didn't eat any chocolate for a whole year.
▸ That's irrelevant. Let's just **stick to** the facts. Where were you last night?
▸ That's my story and I'm **sticking to** it! It's absolutely true.
▸ It's a good essay. It's clear and **sticks to** the point.

Check Use the sentences in the Study box to help you do these exercises.

MEANING

Which two of these might you do if you *stick to* something?

a continue doing something you started
b do lots of different things
c not change your ideas
d change your ideas often

GRAMMAR

Which of these are grammatically possible?

a He always sticks to his principles.
b I'm going to stick my story to.
c She stuck to her plan.
d His principles are always stuck to by him.

→ Now check your answers in the key.

Practise

1 **Match the two halves to make complete sentences.**

a I'm not very adventurous in the kitchen —
b Don't stick to the major roads,
c Even under questioning,
d We'll talk about that later.
e If you're going to go on a diet,

i Let's just stick to one thing at a time.
ii I just stick to what I know I can cook.
iii take a smaller road and you'll go through some nice countryside.
iv make sure you intend to stick to it.
v he stuck to his story about where he was on the night of the crime.

2 **Complete the sentences with one of these phrases.**

to stick to   don't stick to   not sticking to   stuck to   stick to

a The best idea is this: choose a good strategy and _____ it.
b A lot of drivers lose their license for _____ the speed limit.
c This is the agenda for today — we'll try _____ it so we can finish by 5 o'clock.
d Why should we do something different? There's no point having a plan if you _____ it!
e I've always _____ my principles.

→ Now check your answers in the key.

Build your vocabulary

IDIOMS

Stick to your guns means 'to refuse to change your mind about something, even when people disagree with you':
▸ *Everyone thinks I'm mad, but I'm **sticking to my guns**. I know I saw a UFO.*

Stick to the knitting. If a business **sticks to the knitting**, it continues to do what it is good at.

83 stick up for somebody, something or yourself

Study Read these sentences carefully.

▶ It's a group that **sticks up for** farmers' interests.
▶ Thanks for **sticking up for** me when the others were criticizing me.
▶ Nobody **stuck up for** me when I was in trouble.
▶ **Stick up for** what you believe in.
▶ He's able to **stick up for** himself at school.

Check Use the sentences in the Study box to help you do these exercises.

MEANING

Choose the two verbs which best fill the gaps in this explanation of *stick up for*.

support   talk about
choose   defend   like

to _____ or
_____ somebody or
something

GRAMMAR

Which of these are grammatically possible?

a She stuck up for me.
b She was stuck up for.
c She stuck up for her beliefs.
d She stuck up for it.

➔ Now check your answers in the key.

Practise

1 Choose the correct verb form to complete these sentences.

a He was bullied because he couldn't *stick up for / stuck up for* himself.
b She always *sticks up for / was stuck up for* her sister.
c Don't worry — I'll *sticking up for / stick up for* you.
d It's nice to see two brothers *stuck up for / sticking up for* each other.

2 Fill the gaps in these sentences with the correct form of *stick up for somebody or something*.

a It was my mother who _____ me.

b She's not afraid to _____ herself.

c Who will _____ my family if I don't?

d He is really weak and never _____ himself.

e I've always believed in _____ my rights.

f You can't always depend on your friends to _____ you.

g The more I warned her what he was like, the more she _____ him.

➔ Now check your answers in the key.

Build your vocabulary

SYNONYMS   → STAND UP FOR SOMEBODY, SOMETHING OR YOURSELF

84 sum up; sum something up

Study Read these sentences carefully.

▸ To **sum up**, we need to put more money into the project.
▸ How would you **sum up** your experience in Kenya?
▸ She **summed** the situation **up** in a few words.
▸ He made several comments and I had to **sum** them **up**.
▸ The problems have been **summed up** by the inspector in her report.

Check Use the sentences in the Study box to help you do these exercises.

MEANING

If you *sum up*, or *sum something up*, which of these do you do?

a You add several numbers together.
b You give the main details of something in a short and clear way.
c You stop talking.

GRAMMAR

Which of these are grammatically possible?

a I'll sum up the report.
b I'll sum the report up.
c I'll sum up it.
d I'll sum it up.
e The report was summed up.

→ Now check your answers in the key.

Practise

1 Choose the correct form of *sum up* to fill the gaps in the sentences. You will not need to use them all.

summed up   summing up   sum up   summed them up   sum them up

a To _____, he is beginning to make good progress.
b She _____ what we had agreed so far.
c Find the main points of the essay and _____ in the conclusion.
d The judge is just _____ the trial.

2 Complete the speakers' comments in a suitable way, using a form of *sum up* and any other words you need.

a A news reporter is ending a report on a police investigation into an accident.
   To _____, the police do not yet know _____.
b The college principal is finishing her report on the last year.
   Let me _____ it's been a good year for the college.
c 'What was the chairman's message about the state of the company?'
   'Well, he _____ it's doing very well.'
d 'I didn't see the programme on global warming last night. What did they say?'
   'Well, _____, they said that the situation _____.'

→ Now check your answers in the key.

Build your vocabulary

RELATED WORDS   NOUN: ˌsumming-ˈup (This is a countable noun.)
                 ▸ *The judge completed his **summing-up**.*

SYNONYMS   The verb **summarize** means the same as **sum up**:
                 ▸ *Can you **summarize** what was said at the meeting?*

85 take something back

Study Read these sentences carefully.

- I **take back** what I said about her being mean.
- He said it was my fault, and refused to **take** his comments **back**.
- You've said it now and you can't **take** it **back**.
- The statement was **taken back** but the damage had already been done.

Check Use the sentences in the Study box to help you do these exercises.

MEANING

Which of these explanations best fits this meaning of *take something back*?

a to admit that something you said is wrong or that you should not have said it
b to say that what you said is right
c to accuse somebody of saying something that is not true

GRAMMAR

Which of these are grammatically correct?

a I take back everything I said.
b I take my comments back.
c I take back.
d I take it back.
e It was taken back.

→ Now check your answers in the key.

Practise

1 **Rearrange these words to make a correct sentence.**

take   said   back   it   but   was   he   I   unhelpful   I   all

2 **Write sentences using one of the nouns below and a different form of *take back* in each. One has been done for you as an example.**

allegation   remark   statement   comment   criticism

a He refused to take back his remark.
b _____ .
c _____ .
d _____ .
e _____ .

→ Now check your answers in the key.

Build your vocabulary

SYNONYMS   The verbs **retract** and **withdraw** mean the same as **take something back**, but they are formal words:

- *He made a false confession which he later **retracted**.*
- *The newspaper **withdrew** the allegations the next day.*

86 take something **down**

Check Use the sentences in the Study box to help you do these exercises.

MEANING

Which of the following is closest in meaning to *take something down*?

a to move something to a lower position
b to make something shorter
c to write something

GRAMMAR

Which of the following are grammatically possible?

a He took down her phone number.
b He took her phone number down.
c He took it down.
d He took down it.
e Her phone number was taken down.

→ Now check your answers in the key.

Practise

1 Match the two halves to make complete sentences.

a I didn't know which member of staff I had spoken to
b I couldn't return her phone call
c One of the cars sped away from the crash scene
d He took out a notebook

i and took down my name and address.
ii because I'd forgotten to take down her name.
iii because I'd taken down her number wrongly.
iv so I took down its registration number.

2 Rewrite the following sentences, using a form of *take something down* **in each.**

a The police officer wrote down my address in his notebook.

_____

b The reporters were recording every word she said.

_____

c The official sat at a table, making a note of the information Mike was giving him.

_____

→ Now check your answers in the key.

Build your vocabulary

SYNONYMS

note something down:
▶ *I noted down all my friends' email addresses.*

See also **write something down** in *Really Learn 100 Phrasal Verbs*.

87 take somebody in

Study Read these sentences carefully.

▸ It was a huge international fraud that **took in** a lot of people.
▸ He's such a good liar — he **takes** everyone **in**.
▸ She **took** me **in** completely with her story. I believed every word.
▸ How could I have **been taken in** by his charm?

Check Use the sentences in the Study box to help you do these exercises.

MEANING

Which of the following best explains this meaning of *take somebody in*?

a to deceive somebody
b to accept somebody
c to include somebody

GRAMMAR

There is a grammatical mistake in two of these sentences. Find them and correct them.

a He didn't take in you, did he?
b You won't take anyone in with that story!
c He took me completely — I really believed him!
d Helen was completely taken in.

→ Now check your answers in the key.

Practise

1 **Choose the correct form of *take in* to complete these sentences.**

a He can't be trusted — don't let him _____ you _____.
b My father warned me not to be _____ by dishonest salesmen.
c He's such a good actor he _____ me _____ completely.
d Inexperienced magistrates are sometimes _____ by clever criminals.

2 **Rewrite the following sentences so that the meaning stays the same, using the verb *take somebody in*.**

a He deceived us completely with his story about his father being ill.
He _____.
b She told us her purse had been stolen, making us all believe her.
She _____.
c I was surprised at how easy it was to deceive her.
I was surprised _____.

→ Now check your answers in the key.

Build your vocabulary

SYNONYMS

Deceive somebody is more formal:
▸ *She completely **deceived** me with her story.*

OTHER MEANINGS

Take somebody in has several other meanings, for example: 'to allow somebody to stay in your home' or 'to accept somebody as a member, student, patient, etc.':
▸ *When my parents died my uncle **took** me **in**.*
▸ *The college **took in** more students than ever last year.*

SIMILAR VERBS   → FALL FOR SOMETHING

88 take something in

Study Read these sentences carefully.

- She **took in** the situation at a glance and ran for help.
- It's incredible news. I really can't **take** it **in**. Are you sure it's true?
- I've been reading for hours. I'm so tired that I'm not **taking** anything **in** any more.
- The lecturer spoke really fast and it was quite difficult to **take** it all **in**.
- She found it hard to **take in** what he had told her.

Check Use the sentences in the Study box to help you do these exercises.

MEANING

True or false?

a **Take in** can mean 'to understand, remember or believe new information'.

_____

b **Take in** is usually used when it is easy to understand, remember or believe something. _____

GRAMMAR

Which of these are grammatically possible?

a I really can't take it in.
b At first, he couldn't take in.
c It's hard to take it in.
d He was unable to take in it.

→ Now check your answers in the key.

Practise

1 **Choose the right phrase to make a sentence.**

a There was so much information *taking in/to take in* that I didn't learn much.
b Do you think you *took in/take in* much of what they were telling us?
c It's been a real shock — I haven't *taken it all in/been taken in* yet.
d I don't think I'll ever really *be able to take in/can take in* the news.

2 **Rewrite these sentences using a suitable form of *take something in*. The first one has been done for you.**

a A lot of the lecture this morning was too difficult for me to understand.
A lot of the lecture was too difficult to take in.

b She did tell me her name, but I didn't really pay attention to what she was saying.
She did tell me her name, but I _____.

c I was shocked and at first I didn't realize what had happened.
I was shocked _____.

→ Now check your answers in the key.

Build your vocabulary

SIMILAR VERBS **Sink in** has a similar meaning but is used in a different way:
- *We're getting married! I don't think I've **taken** it **in** yet!*
- *We're getting married! I don't think it's **sunk in** yet!*

Notice that it is the news or the information that is the subject of the verb.

89 take something **out**; take something **out of** something

Study Read these sentences carefully.
- He felt in his pocket and **took out** his keys.
- It won't work if you **take** the batteries **out**.
- He was caught **taking** money **out of** the till.
- That's my phone! Did you **take** it **out of** my drawer?
- You can **take** three books **out** at a time.
- These books cannot be **taken out of** the library.

Check Use the sentences in the Study box to help you do these exercises.

MEANING

Which of these sentences best explains this meaning of *take something out*?

a To borrow something from somewhere.
b To remove something from somewhere.
c To show something to somebody.

GRAMMAR

There is a grammatical mistake in one of the following sentences. Find it and correct it.

a She took out her keys.
b She took out her keys of her pocket.
c She took them out.
d She took £200 out of the bank.
e She took £200 out.

→ Now check your answers in the key.

Practise

Use the correct form of *take out* **or** *take out of* **and one of the nouns or pronouns below to complete these sentences.**

libraries   cash   them   the laptop

a I had a long wait at the airport, so I _____ and started to write my report.

b Too many books are _____ and not returned.

c If you _____ with a credit card, you'll have to pay interest.

d Keep fireworks in a metal box and _____ one at a time.

→ Now check your answers in the key.

Build your vocabulary

SYNONYMS   You can also use **withdraw** when talking about taking money out of a bank. It is slightly more formal:
- He **withdrew** *$450 from the bank.*

OPPOSITES   If you put money into your bank account, you can use the verb **pay in**:
- I **paid in** *£500 this morning.*

Use **take back** or **return** to refer to library books:
- I need to **take** these books **back** to the library.

OTHER MEANINGS   You can also use **take out** when you arrange a loan, insurance or a mortgage:
- He had to **take out** *a huge loan to repay his debts.*

90 take to somebody or something

Study Read these sentences carefully.

- She never **takes to** her son's girlfriends.
- He's **taken to** his new school very quickly.
- Jack is a great coach and I'll be amazed if the team doesn't **take to** him at once.
- I tried to learn the piano, but I never really **took to** it.

Check Use the sentences in the Study box to help you do these exercises.

MEANING

Which of the following is closest
in meaning to *take to somebody or
something*?

a start disliking somebody or
something
b steal somebody or something
c start liking somebody or something

GRAMMAR

Which of these are grammatically
possible?

a She took to Peter at once.
b She took to him at once.
c She took Peter to at once.
d She took him to very quickly.
e Peter was taken to very quickly.

→ Now check your answers in the key.

Practise

1 Complete the sentences with an appropriate form of *take to*.

a At first Max didn't _____ his new teacher.

b She has really _____ science.

c Give it a go and see if you _____ it.

d She seems to be _____ the new job.

e I'm sorry the baby's crying so much. She just doesn't _____
strangers.

2 Complete the sentences by using the correct form of *take to* and one of the three
possible nouns or pronouns.

a She didn't like school and never _____ her *school / studying / teachers*.

b Most of the team _____ the new *offices / boss / emails* straight
away.

c I thought the two kids would get on well, but they didn't _____
themselves / him / each other at all.

→ Now check your answers in the key.

Build your vocabulary

IDIOMS

Not take kindly to something means 'to not like something':
- *She didn't take kindly to being told what to do.*

OPPOSITES

To **take against somebody or something**:
- *Why have you suddenly taken against Laura?*

OTHER MEANINGS

To **take to something** also means 'to develop an ability for
something':
- *If you take to the work, we'll give you a job here.*

91 tear something up

Study Read these sentences carefully.

- ▸ He **tore up** all the letters from his ex-wife.
- ▸ She had **torn** an old sheet **up** to make bandages.
- ▸ If you don't need the papers any more, **tear** them **up** and put them in the bin.
- ▸ The photograph had been **torn up**.

Check Use the sentences in the Study box to help you do these exercises.

MEANING

Choose the <u>three</u> best words to complete this meaning of *tear something up*.

wood   paper   cloth   plastic   china

to destroy _____,

_____ or _____

by pulling it into lots of small pieces

GRAMMAR

Which of these are grammatically possible?

a He tore up the paper.
b He was tearing the paper up.
c He tore it up.
d He tore up it.
e The paper had been torn up.

→ Now check your answers in the key.

Practise

1 Fill the gaps in this article with appropriate forms of *tear something up*.

Protecting your money. You should always be very careful to protect yourself from possible fraud. This means _____ documents such as bills and bank statements when you have finished with them. Memorize your PIN when it arrives, then _____ or shred the letter. If you have written a cheque that you are not going to use, don't forget to _____. Make sure any unwanted personal information is promptly _____.

2 Write a sentence using a form of *tear something up*, saying if and when you would destroy each thing or if you would keep it.

a a photograph of yourself that you don't like

_____

b an old phone bill

_____

c a contract relating to your job

_____

d paper that a gift is wrapped in

_____

→ Now check your answers in the key.

Build your vocabulary

SYNONYMS   To **rip something up** is often used when somebody does it suddenly or violently:
▸ *She angrily **ripped** the letter **up** and threw it in the bin.*

92 throw somebody out;
throw somebody out of somewhere

Study Read these sentences carefully.

▶ At the pool today, we had to **throw** several kids **out** for behaving badly.
▶ The country has had elections and **has thrown out** its socialist government.
▶ It's the kind of company where they **throw** you **out** if they don't think you're good enough.
▶ She got **thrown out** for cheating.
▶ He was **thrown out of** college in the first semester.

Check Use the sentences in the Study box to help you do these exercises.

MEANING

If you *throw somebody out*, do you:

a ask them politely to leave?
b pick them up and throw them through the air?
c use force or your authority to make them go?

GRAMMAR

Which of these are grammatically correct?

a They threw Jake out of college.
b They threw out Jake of college.
c The threw him out.
d They threw out him.
e He was thrown out of.
f He was thrown out.

→ Now check your answers in the key.

Practise

1 Three of these sentences are about people being *thrown out*. Which three?

a My wife asked me to go out and get some milk.
b My brother's firm fired him because he sent offensive emails.
c They made me leave the country because I had stayed too long.
d His wife told him she didn't want him to live there any more.
e I don't shop at that store now. It's too expensive.

2 Rewrite these three sentences from Exercise 1 without changing the meaning, using the right form of *throw somebody out* in each.

_____

_____

_____

→ Now check your answers in the key.

Build your vocabulary

SYNONYMS

Boot somebody out (of somewhere) and **kick somebody out** (of somewhere). These are informal verbs:

▶ *I got **booted out of** the junior band because I played too many wrong notes!*

OTHER MEANINGS This verb can also mean 'to reject a proposal or an idea':

▶ *The committee have **thrown out** the plans for a new hypermarket.*

SIMILAR VERBS Look at **throw something away** in *Really Learn 100 Phrasal Verbs.*

93 try something on

Study Read these sentences carefully.

- ▸ Sometimes we go to the mall and **try on** clothes we can't afford.
- ▸ I hate **trying** hats **on** — I always think I look terrible!
- ▸ What a fabulous dress! Why don't you **try it on**?
- ▸ Shoes and boots must be **tried on** over socks or stockings.

Check Use the sentences in the Study box to help you do these exercises.

MEANING

Why do you *try on* clothes and shoes?

a To see if they are new.
b To see if you can afford them.
c To see if you like them and if they fit.

GRAMMAR

Two of these sentences contain grammatical errors. Find and correct them.

a I love trying on clothes.
b I love trying on.
c I love trying clothes on.
d I love trying on them.
e Clothes can be tried on here.

→ Now check your answers in the key.

Practise

1 What do you think is being *tried on* here?

a It's too long — I'll trip over it when I walk. _____

b They're too tight. I can't fasten the waist. _____

c Mmm — I think it's too big. You can't see my face underneath. _____

d I love them but I'll fall over on those heels. _____

e I'd better get a larger size so I can wear a thick jumper underneath. _____

2 Complete the sentences with a suitable form of *try on*, making any changes you need to.

a I had to drag him to the store, but then he insisted on _____ every pair in the place.

b I don't know what to wear tonight! I _____ everything I own but nothing looks right.

c She was fired for _____ guests' fur coats.

d The trousers looked fine when I _____ them, but I don't like them now I've got them home.

→ Now check your answers in the key.

Build your vocabulary

OTHER MEANINGS **Try it on** can also mean 'to behave badly towards somebody, especially to see how far you can go':
- ▸ *The kids sometimes **try it on** with a new babysitter.*

SIMILAR VERBS You can also use **try something on somebody**:
- ▸ *I'm knitting Em a jumper but I think I'd better **try it on** her in case it's too long.*

94 try something or somebody out

Study Read these sentences carefully.

▶ I'm **trying out** a different gym.
▶ Shall we **try** that new café **out** today?
▶ I have an idea and I'd like to **try** it **out** on you.
▶ We've been **trying out** some new musicians for our band.
▶ The drug has not **been tried out** on humans yet.

Check Use the sentences in the Study box to help you do these exercises.

MEANING

Answer 'yes' or 'no' to the questions about this meaning of *try out*.

a If you **try** a place **out**, have you been there before? _____

b If you **try** somebody **out**, do you know that he or she will definitely be useful to you? _____

c If you **try** something **out**, is this to help you make up your mind about it? _____

GRAMMAR

Which of these are grammatically possible?

a He tried the bed out.
b He tried out the bed.
c He tried out it.
d He tried it out.
e The bed was tried out.

→ Now check your answers in the key.

Practise

1 Complete the following sentences using a form of *try out* and one of the words or phrases below.

a few different jobs   a new type of hose   it   him

a There's this new hair salon and they're looking for volunteers to _____.
b She _____ before deciding to become a teacher.
c _____ by fire fighters.
d We decided to _____ and gave him a job in our store.

2 Complete the responses to the following statements using a form of *try out* in your answer and any other words you need.

a I don't like doing things I've never done before.
   You shouldn't be afraid to _____.
b Where shall we go for lunch?
   Why don't we _____.

→ Now check your answers in the key.

Build your vocabulary

RELATED WORDS   NOUN: 'tryout

▶ *You can come and work for me as a **tryout**.*

SIMILAR VERBS   **Try out (for something)** means 'to compete for a place in a sports team, a part in a play, etc.' and is used especially in American English:

▶ *He **tried out** for the school band.*

95 turn into something;
turn something into something

Study Read these sentences carefully.

- The discussion **turned into** a heated argument.
- He **turned into** a very bitter man after his divorce.
- They **turned** the spare bedroom **into** a study.
- It was originally a book but they've **turned** it **into** a movie.
- The bank has been **turned into** a nightclub.

Check Use the sentences in the Study box to help you do these exercises.

MEANING

If something *turns into* something else, or you *turn it into* something else, does it:

a stay the same?
b move to a different place?
c change and become something else?

GRAMMAR

There is a grammatical error in one of these sentences. Find it and correct it.

a The old library was turned into apartments.
b They turned it into apartments.
c They turned the old library into apartments.
d They turned apartments into it.

→ Now check your answers in the key.

Practise

1 Match the two halves to make complete sentences.

a Our dream trip turned into a nightmare
b It had been a wet morning
c Her love for him
d She turned into a very greedy woman
e After only a few years

i but it was turning into a bright, sunny afternoon.
ii when we had our money and passports stolen.
iii after she married him.
iv he had turned the company into a market leader.
v was quickly turning into hate.

2 Answer the questions using a form of *turn into something* or *turn something into something* and one of the nouns below.

a parking lot   a prince   a bitter row

a Do you know the story about the princess and the frog?

   Do you mean the frog that _____?

b Are Jack and Helen getting on better together now?

   No, every conversation they have _____.

c What has happened to the park?

   It's been sold and _____.

→ Now check your answers in the key.

Build your vocabulary

SYNONYMS   The phrasal verb **change into** means the same as **turn into** and is used in the same way:

- *We've **changed** the spare bedroom **into** a home office.*

96 turn out (1)

Study Read these sentences carefully.

- ▸ The situation looks bad but these things normally **turn out** OK.
- ▸ How do you think the discussions will **turn out**?
- ▸ Your mother would be proud of how you kids have **turned out**.
- ▸ 'You've done a great job on the project.' 'Yes, it's **turning out** really well.'

Check Use the sentences in the Study box to help you do these exercises.

MEANING

Which **one** of the following does **not** explain this meaning of *turn out*?

a to speak in a particular way
b to happen in a particular way
c to end in a particular way

GRAMMAR

Which of these are grammatically possible?

a Everything turned out OK.
b How will things turn out?
c She turned out the discussions very well.
d The election was turned out to be a success.

→ Now check your answers in the key.

Practise

1 Match the two halves to make complete sentences.

a When you have children
b You need to get qualifications
c We all thought we'd have a great time
d I hate having my photo taken

i but it turned out better than I expected!
ii but it turned out differently.
iii you never know how they will turn out.
iv in case your football career doesn't turn out well.

2 Write a suitable question or comment to complete the dialogue, using a form of *turn out* and any other words you need.

a _____?

It was terrible. Nobody spoke to me. I wish I hadn't taken the job now!

b _____.

I hope you're right. I won't give up too soon anyway.

c Did you enjoy your leaving party at your last job?

I did! I wasn't expecting to, but _____.

→ Now check your answers in the key.

Build your vocabulary

IDIOMS

Turn out for the best. For the best here means 'well':
- ▸ *Getting fired was hard, but I'm sure it will all* **turn out for the best**.

OTHER MEANINGS

When **turn out** is used with **that** or **to be/do, etc.**, it means 'to be discovered or to prove to be something':
- ▸ *It* **turned out that** *Sarah was a friend of my sister.*
- ▸ *My decision* **turned out to have been** *a mistake.*

97 turn out (2)

Study Read these sentences carefully.

▸ A big crowd always **turns out** for the fair.
▸ The whole town **turned out** to watch what was happening.
▸ The movie has been a flop. Only about ten people have **turned out** to see it.
▸ The government are finding ways to persuade more voters to **turn out**.

Check Use the sentences in the Study box to help you do these exercises.

MEANING

Choose the two best verbs to complete this meaning of *turn out*.

attend   ignore   leave   go to

to _____ or to

_____ something,

especially an event

GRAMMAR

Which of these are grammatically possible?

a Thousands of people turned out.
b Why didn't anybody turn out?
c The game turned out a crowd.
d An enormous crowd was turned out.

→ Now check your answers in the key.

Practise

1 Look at the pictures of seats in a concert hall. Black squares are occupied seats. White squares are empty seats. How many people *turned out* on each night of the concert? Write a sentence about each night, using the verb *turn out*.

a _____

b _____

c _____

d _____

Thursday

Friday

Saturday

Sunday

2 Complete the following sentences in an appropriate way, using a form of *turn out* and any other necessary information.

a The newspapers said no one would go to the funeral but in fact the whole town _____ .

b It is the country's first presidential election tomorrow and I think almost everyone _____ .

c When it rains at the festival, everyone still _____ .

→ Now check your answers in the key.

Build your vocabulary

RELATED WORDS   NOUN: 'turnout (= the number of people who attend an event or vote in an election) (This is usually used in the singular.)
▸ *The turnout for the election was very high.*

IDIOMS   Turn out in force. This emphasizes that a large number of people attend:
▸ *The fans turned out in force to support the team.*

98 walk out; walk out of something

Study Read these sentences carefully.

- ▸ If anyone insulted me in a meeting, I would **walk out**.
- ▸ Some of the audience **walked out** in disgust.
- ▸ Several students **walked out of** the debate before the vote.

Check Use the sentences in the Study box to help you do these exercises.

MEANING

Use three of the words below to complete this meaning of walk out.

angry   finish   leave
end   bored   start

to _____ a meeting,

performance, etc. suddenly before the

_____ because you do not

like it or are _____ .

→ Now check your answers in the key.

GRAMMAR

Which of these are grammatically possible?

a She walked out of the meeting.
b She walked out the meeting of.
c She walked it out of.
d She walked out of it.
e She walked out.

Practise

1 In which of the following situations might you *walk out*?

a You are at a concert which has just finished.
b You are at a conference but do not like what the speaker is saying.
c You are having a job interview and you need to use the bathroom.
d Somebody says something that offends you at a meeting.
e You are enjoying a party, but need to leave early.

2 Complete the following sentences with the correct form of *walk out* and a suitable noun if necessary.

a Everyone was arguing fiercely and the speaker _____ in a temper.
b If your students behave really badly, just _____ .
c The movie was so violent some people started _____ .
d The chairman was so rude to me I thought about _____ .
e She once _____ a job interview because they asked her if she was married.

→ Now check your answers in the key.

Build your vocabulary

RELATED WORDS   NOUN: 'walkout (This is a countable noun.)

OTHER MEANINGS   To **walk out** is used when workers go on strike:

▸ *Workers threatened to **walk out** in protest over pay cuts.*

The noun **walkout** is also related to this meaning.

99 walk out; walk out on somebody or something

Study Read these sentences carefully.

▸ I should have **walked out** rather than agree to the deal.
▸ How could he **walk out on** his family like that?
▸ The government have **walked out on** the partnership.
▸ Employers don't like you **walking out on** them as soon as they have finished training you.
▸ He said there was nothing in his life that he wouldn't **walk out on**.

Check Use the sentences in the Study box to help you do these exercises.

MEANING

If you *walk out on* somebody or something, which <u>one</u> of these do you do?

a go with somebody somewhere
b argue with somebody
c leave a person or a place
d protest about something

GRAMMAR

Which of these are grammatically possible?

a He walked out on his wife.
b He walked her out on.
c He walked out on her.
d He walked out.
e His wife was walked out on.

→ Now check your answers in the key.

Practise

1 **Who is referred to by the pronoun in bold in the following sentences?**

a They had only been married a year when he walked out on **her**.
b **They** blamed themselves when their father walked out.
c Thirty years after their wedding, she walked out on **him**.
d She was good at the job, so **they** were amazed when she walked out on them.

2 **Complete the following sentences using a form of *walk out (on)* and one of the objects below where necessary.**

his colleagues   me   chat show hosts

a After four years in a violent marriage, she has finally _____.

b She's a big star, but she has a reputation for _____.

c I thought we were getting on well. I never thought he would just _____

_____.

d He never apologized for _____ in the middle of a big project.

3 **Rewrite the words in *italics* using a form of *walk out on*.**

a He's a great footballer, *but he left his country and went to play abroad.*
b *That was the only job I've ever suddenly left.*
c Whatever happens, *I will never abandon the band in the middle of a tour.*
d She had become bored with her life, *so she split up with her husband.*

→ Now check your answers in the key.

100 wrap something up;
wrap somebody or yourself up

Study Read these sentences carefully.
- My mother always **wrapped up** gifts for us in beautiful paper.
- Make sure you **wrap** the books **up** well before you mail them.
- This is such an odd shape. How am I going to **wrap** it **up**?
- If the book is a gift, it can **be wrapped up** in the store for a small charge.
- **Wrap** the baby **up** in a blanket if you're going out — it's freezing outside.
- Look, there's Billy — all **wrapped up** in a warm coat, a hat and two scarves!

Check Use the sentences in the Study box to help you do these exercises.

MEANING

Are the following sentences true or false?

a In the first four sentences, **wrap something up** means to put something inside some paper or packaging, especially when you are giving or sending something. _____

b If you **wrap somebody or yourself up**, you put on clothes that are fashionable. _____

GRAMMAR

There is <u>one</u> mistake in the following sentences. Find it and correct it.

a Wrap the book up in brown paper.
b She wrapped up the book beautifully.
c Make sure it's well wrapped up.
d She often forgets to wrap himself up in warm clothes.
e It wasn't wrapped up properly.

→ Now check your answers in the key.

Practise

1 Match the two halves to make complete sentences or comments.

a I've bought him some gifts
b Wrap up properly today —
c Look at that!
d It was wrapped up so securely

i that I couldn't open the package.
ii why don't you take a scarf?
iii but they are too difficult to wrap up!
iv The dog is wrapped up in an overcoat.

2 Find and correct the mistakes in these sentences.

a Why do grocery stores wrap goods so securely up?
b She's all wrap up for winter!
c In Japan, wrap up gifts is almost a form of art.
d I wrapped the twins up on hats and scarves before they went out.

→ Now check your answers in the key.

Build your vocabulary

SIMILAR VERBS To **wrap something** can be used with the same meaning:
- We **wrapped** the baby in a blanket and put her in the car.

OTHER MEANINGS To **wrap something up** can also mean 'to complete something successfully':
- OK, that's everything. I think we can **wrap up** the meeting now.

To be **wrapped up in something or somebody** means 'to be so interested in one thing that you ignore others':
- He's totally **wrapped up** in his family.

Key to exercises

1 ˌadd ˈup
to seem reasonable; to make sense; to have all the different parts agreeing with each other

Check
MEANING: reasonable, sensible   NOTE This verb is often used with a negative.
GRAMMAR: a, c

Practise
1 a ii b i c iv d iii 2 a add up b adds up c add up d added up e didn't add up f to add up

2 ˌadd ˈup; ˌadd sth ˈup
to calculate the total of two or more numbers or amounts

Check
MEANING: c
GRAMMAR: a, b, d, e

Practise
1 a added up b adding them up c was added up d will add up 2 Suggested Answers: a I don't know, we haven't *added* it *up* yet. b Yes certainly. I'll just *add* it *up*.

3 ˌback sb/sth ˈup
to say or show that what sb says is true; to support or help sb/sth

Check
MEANING: b
GRAMMAR: b, c, d NOTE The pattern *back these claims up* is rare.

Practise
1 a their findings b examples c what you say d the accusations 2 a ...who can *back up* what you're saying? b ...he would definitely *back* me *up* (on this). c ...but they are in fact *backed up* by most...
NOTE See also **back something up** in *Really Learn 100 Phrasal Verbs for Business*.

4 ˌbe ˈover
to have finished

Check
MEANING: c
GRAMMAR: b NOTE This verb is not used in the progressive tenses.

Practise
1 a I didn't want the evening to be over. b He wouldn't comment until the trial was over. c Our troubles will soon be over/Soon our troubles will be over. 2 Suggested Answers: a Don't worry, the project *is* nearly *over*/will soon *be over*. b Because my marriage *was over*. c I felt as though my life *was over*. d When the meeting *is over*.

5 ˌblow sth ˈup
to fill sth with air or gas

Check
MEANING: 1 gas, air 2 b, e
GRAMMAR: a, b, c, e

Practise
Suggested Answers: a No, the balloons still need to be *blown up*. b Yes, I had to *blow up* your back tyre. c We *will blow up* the air mattress for him.

6 ˌbreak sth ˈoff
to end something suddenly

Check
MEANING: c
GRAMMAR: a, c, d

Practise
1 a broken off b broke off c break off 2 end: Leaders decided to *break off* discussions...
NOTE See also **break down** in *Really Learn 100 Phrasal Verbs for Business*.

7 ˌbreak ˈout
if something bad **breaks out**, it starts

Check
MEANING: 1 start 2 a party
GRAMMAR: a, b

Practise
1 Suggested Answers: a The fight broke out in the middle of the street. b Trouble broke out between groups... c A dangerous virus has broken out among... 2 Suggested Answers: Riots *broke out* in several parts of the city last night. A fierce debate *has broken out* over the issue of ID cards.

8 ˌbreak ˈout; ˌbreak ˈout of sth
to escape from a place or situation, especially from prison

Check
MEANING: a
GRAMMAR: d He broke out of jail.

Practise
1 a break out of b have broken out of c break out of d broke out 2 Suggested Answers: I would improve security so it is more difficult for prisoners to *break out of* prison. I would improve conditions so prisoners did not feel they wanted to *break out*.

9 ˌbring sth aˈbout
to make sth happen

Check
MEANING: b
GRAMMAR: a, b, d NOTE The pattern *bring changes about* is very rare.

Practise
1 a ii b iii c iv d i 2 Suggested Answers: a Changes in the weather *brings about*/can *bring about* changes in our mood. b The government wants to *bring about* a reduction in tobacco consumption. c The failure of the business *was brought about* by a worldwide recession. d What *brought about* the collapse of the company? e Expecting problems can play an important part in *bringing* them *about*.

10 ˌbring sth ˈback
to make sth that existed or was done before be used or done again

Check
MEANING: existed, before, used, again
GRAMMAR: a, c, d

Practise
1 a brought back b brought back c bring back d bring it back 2 a ...they should *bring back* national service. b ...you suggest *bringing* it *back*? c ...wanting to *bring* beating *back*!

11 ˌbring sth ˈdown

to reduce the price, number or level of something

Check
MEANING: c
GRAMMAR: c They've brought prices down to £13.99.

Practise
1 a The airline has brought down the cost of flights by 15%. **b** We're bringing down the price to/by £25. **c** They will bring down the price from £30 to £25. **2 a** Interest rates *have been brought down*. **b** We plan to *bring down* our prices/*bring* our prices *down*. **c** The rate *has been brought down* by 20%.

12 ˌbrush sthˈup; ˌbrush ˈup on sth

to study or practise sth in order to get back the skill or knowledge that you had in the past but have not used for some time

Check
MEANING: b
GRAMMAR: a, b, c

Practise
1 a The staff have been *brushing up on* what to do... **b** Are you *brushing up on it/brushing it up* tonight? **c** He will have to *brush up (on)* his writing if... **d** ...but they have *brushed up on* it now. **2** Suggested Answers: I could *brush it up* by reading newspapers in English. Revising phrasal verbs will help me *brush up on* my English.

13 ˌcall sth ˈoff

to decide that sth will not happen or continue

Check
MEANING: b
GRAMMAR: c The search was called off.

Practise
1 a called off **b** called off **c** been called off **d** call off **e** was called off **2** Suggested Answers: I'm going to have to *call off* the...because...

14 ˌcalm ˈdown; ˌcalm sb/sth/yourself ˈdown

if sb **calms down**, or you **calm them down**, they stop being angry or excited and become calm; if a situation **calms down** or sb/sth **calms it down** it becomes calmer

Check
MEANING: b, c
GRAMMAR: **a** Calm down. **b** She couldn't calm herself down. **c** ...had to take deep breaths to calm myself down. **d** Correct. NOTE This verb is not often used in the passive.

Practise
1 a It can be really difficult *to* calm down... **b** ...take a deep breath *and* calm down please? **c** ...Can't you calm *them* down? **2** Suggested Answers: **a** If you don't *calm down*, I... **b** ...I listen to my favourite music to *calm myself down*. **c** ...and got his team *calmed down/calmed* his team *down*.

15 ˌclear ˈup; ˌclear sth ˈup

to make something clean and neat

Check
MEANING: clean, neat
GRAMMAR: a, b, c, e

Practise
1 a iv **b** iii **c** i **d** v **e** ii **2** Suggested Answers: **a** Can you *clear* it *up*, please? **b** ...so I will *clear* my desk *up/clear* everything *up* before I go. **c** Who pays to *clear* it *up*?

16 ˌclear sth ˈup

to solve or explain sth that is mysterious or confusing

Check
MEANING: **1** b **2** anger
GRAMMAR: b, c, e

Practise
1 a clear up **b** cleared up **c** clear up **d** cleared up **e** be cleared up **f** cleared up **g** clear up **2** Suggested Answers: We need to try and *clear up* any confusion as quickly as possible. I'm glad we've *cleared* that misunderstanding *up*.

17 ˌcome ˈup against sth

to have to deal with a problem or difficult situation

Check
MEANING: **1** b **2** a, c, d, f
GRAMMAR: a, c

Practise
1 a came up against **b** come up against **c** come up against **d** came up against **e** to come up against **f** come up against it

18 ˌcome ˈup with sth

to think of an idea, an answer to a question or a solution to a problem

Check
MEANING: c
GRAMMAR: a, b

Practise
1 a come up with; ii **b** have come up with; vi **c** coming up with; i **d** come up with; iv **e** come up with; v **f** come up with; iii **2** Suggested Answers: **a** My wife's brilliant at *coming up with* new recipes. **b** I've just *come up with* a really good joke. **c** Let me know if you *come up with* anything else. **d** We've got to *come up with* a solution as soon as possible.

19 conˈsist of sth

to be formed from the things or people mentioned

Check
MEANING: **a** true **b** true **c** false
GRAMMAR: a, c NOTE This verb is not used in the progressive tenses or in the passive.

Practise
1 a contains **b** consists of **c** consist of **d** contained **2 a** iii **b** i **c** ii

20 ˈcount on sb/sth

to rely on sb to do sth; to expect sth to happen and make plans in an appropriate way

Check
MEANING: c
GRAMMAR: a, c, e

Practise
1 a We are counting on the (new) factory to create thousands of (new) jobs. **b** You can count on the public's support. **c** Don't count on him arriving before 7 p.m. **2 a** ...you can always count on us to help you. **b** I'm not

counting on (getting)... **c** ...I was counting on him to be/being here.

21 ₁do a'way with sth/sb
to get rid of sth/sb; to make sth no longer necessary

Check
MEANING: a **a** b **b** c **a**
GRAMMAR: **a** They did away with their garage. **b** They did away with it. **c** They did away with the garage. **d** The garage was done away with.

Practise
1 a ii **b** iii **c** i **2** Suggested Answers: **a** ...so we decided to *do away with* it. **b** He...thinks we should *do away with* hunting. **c** ...and want to *do away with* secrecy. **d** ...that these outdated laws *were done away with*.

22 ₁do with'out; ₁do with'out sb/sth
to manage without somebody or something

Check
MEANING: c
GRAMMAR: **c** I couldn't do without it.

Practise
1 a If there's not enough, you'll have to do without. **b** We couldn't afford a TV so we did without. **c** I did without because there wasn't enough. **2** Suggested Answers: I couldn't *do without* my MP3 player because I listen to it every day on the bus. I could easily *do without* a newspaper because I can check the news on the Internet.

23 ₁drop 'out; ₁drop 'out of sth
to stop taking part in an activity, being a member of a group, etc.; to leave school, college, university, etc. without finishing your studies; to reject the accepted ideas, morals and values of society

Check
MEANING: c
GRAMMAR: a, c

Practise
1 a have dropped out of **b** going to drop out **c** dropped out of **d** we have to drop out of **2** Suggested Answers: I thought about *dropping out of* my university course, but in the end I didn't.

24 ₁eat sth 'up (1)
to eat all of sth

Check
MEANING: a
GRAMMAR: a, b, c, d

Practise
1 a ate up **b** eat up **c** eaten up **d** eating up **e** ate it all up **2** Suggested Answers: **a** ...I *ate* it all *up*. **b** ...he didn't *eat up* his dinner. **c** Who *ate* it *up*?

25 ₁eat sth 'up (2)
to use large quantities of sth, for example fuel or electricity

Check
MEANING: b
GRAMMAR: a, b, c, e

Practise
1 a eats up/will eat up **b** is eaten up/was eaten up **c** eats up **d** ate up/had eaten up/were eating up **2** Suggested Answers: The rent *eats up* nearly half her money. The money she has to pay on bills *doesn't eat up* much.

26 ₁face 'up to sb/sth
to accept and deal with a difficult or unpleasant situation

Check
MEANING: c
GRAMMAR: a, c, d

Practise
1 a, c **2 a** to face up to **b** face up to **c** to face up to **d** Facing up to **e** facing up to **f** face up to

27 ₁fall 'back on sb/sth
to use sb/sth when the situation is difficult or other people/things have failed

Check
MEANING: b
GRAMMAR: a, b

Practise
1 a iv **b** ii **c** i **d** iii **2 a** fell back on **b** fall back on **c** fell back on (talking about) **d** falling back on

28 'fall for sth
to be tricked into believing sth is true when it is not

Check
MEANING: **1 a** untrue **b** yes **2** b
GRAMMAR: a, c, e NOTE This verb is not used in the passive.

Practise
a ...I'm stupid enough to fall for that... **b** I fell for the advert... **c** Everyone fell for the propaganda... **d** ...they didn't fall for his false claim... **e** I'm not the sort of parent who falls for the argument that...

29 ₁fall 'out; ₁fall 'out with sb
to have an argument with sb and stop being friendly with them

Check
MEANING: a
GRAMMAR: **d** They fell out over money.

Practise
1 a with **b** over **c** with, over **2** Suggested Answers: **a** I *fell out with* my tutor. **b** We *fell out over* the time for my tutorial. **c** I don't want to *fall out with* you too!

30 ₁fit 'in; ₁fit 'in with sb/sth
to live or work easily and naturally with a group of people

Check
MEANING: c
GRAMMAR: a, b, c

Practise
1 a fit in with **b** to fit in **c** fitted in/was fitting in **d** fit in **2** Suggested Answers: I didn't find it easy to *fit in* at school.

31 ₁fit sb/sth 'in; ₁fit sb/sth 'into sth
to manage to find time to see sb or to do sth

Check
MEANING: a
GRAMMAR: a, c, e

Practise
1 a ...so I can't fit you in. **b** We can fit in five appointments/fit five appointments in... **2** Suggested Answers: Dr. Stanley can *fit in* an appointment with a new patient at 3.30/between 3.30 and 4.30.

32 ₁get a¹round to sth; ₁get a¹round to doing sth

to find the time to do sth

Check
MEANING: c
GRAMMAR: a, b

Practise
1 a haven't got around to; iii **b** getting around to; ii **c** will get around to; v **d** get around to; iv **e** will get/(has) got around to; i **2** Suggested Answers: We still haven't *got around to* painting the bathroom. I must *get around to* writing that essay.

33 ₁get a¹way with sth

to do sth wrong and not be punished or criticized for it

Check
MEANING: b
GRAMMAR: a, b, d

Practise
1 a get away with **b** gets away with **c** got away with **d** get away with **2** Suggested Answers: **a** She didn't *get away with* not paying her taxes. **b** He *got away with* stealing the money. **c** The kids didn't *get away with* drawing all over the walls. **d** He *got away with* touching the ball with his hand.

34 ₁get ¹by

to manage to live or do sth using the money, knowledge, equipment, etc. that you have, especially when it is not much

Check
MEANING: c
GRAMMAR: c How do they get by on such a small salary?

Practise
1 a get by **b** get by on **c** get by on/got by on **d** get by without **e** got by with **2** Suggested Answers: I couldn't *get by* without a computer because I use it for my work. I could probably *get by* without a washing machine, but only if my mum did my washing for me!

35 ₁get sb ¹down

if sth **gets** you **down**, it makes you feel unhappy or depressed

Check
MEANING: b
GRAMMAR: a, b, c NOTE The object of this verb is usually a pronoun.

Practise
1 a iii **b** i **c** ii **2** Suggested Answers: Jane's money worries *are getting* her *down*. **3** Suggested Answers: Having to work so hard *gets* me *down* sometimes.

36 ₁get ¹over sth

to deal with or gain control of sth

Check
MEANING: b
GRAMMAR: a, b, e

Practise
1 b, c **2 a** ...is getting over bad driving habits. **b** ...breathing exercises can help you get over your nerves. **c** ...but he soon got over it. **d** ...until he gets over his fear of heights.

37 ₁get sth ¹over; ₁get sth ¹over with

to complete sth necessary and usually unpleasant

Check
MEANING: b
GRAMMAR: a, b, d NOTE This verb is not used in the passive or in the pattern *get over something*.

Practise
1 a i **b** iv **c** ii **d** iii **2 a** ...to get them over (with)... **b** Get the housework over (with)... **c** ...they wanted to get the test over with quickly. **d** ...and get it over with!

38 ₁give ¹In; ₁give ¹in to sb/sth

to finally agree to do sth that you do not want to do

Check
MEANING: **1** b **2** b
GRAMMAR: a, b, c, e

Practise
1 a iii **b** v **c** i **d** ii **e** iv **2** Suggested Answers: **a** ...that I finally *gave in to* him. **b** ...and I don't *give in to* anyone. **c** ...they will usually *give in*.

39 ₁go ¹down (1)

if something **goes down** well or badly, people think it is good or bad

Check
MEANING: b
GRAMMAR: a, c, d NOTE This verb is always used with an adverb or an adverbial phrase.

Practise
1 a go down **b** went down **c** go down **2** Suggested Answers: **a** This would *go down very well* with my parents. **b** This would *go down very badly*/This would not *go down well* with my family. **c** This would *go down well* with my wife.
NOTE See also **go down** in *Really Learn 100 Phrasal Verbs for Business*.

40 ₁go ¹down (2)

if a computer **goes down**, it suddenly stops working for a period of time

Check
MEANING: a
GRAMMAR: a, c

Practise
1 a went down **b** goes down **c** had gone down **d** goes down **e** is going down **2** Suggested Answers: **a** Because the computer *went down*. **b** Because I lost all my work when the hard drive *went down*.

41 ₁go ¹in for sth

to like sth and regularly use it, do it, etc.; to have sth as an interest or a hobby

Check
MEANING: a often, like **b** negative
GRAMMAR: b, d

Practise
1 a ii **b** iv **c** iii **d** i **2** Suggested Answers: **a** ...did you *go in for* when you were a teenager? **b** He's always *gone in for* (visiting) places that tourists don't visit. **c** She doesn't really *go in for* (wearing) lots of make-up. **d** I've never *gone in for* (wearing) black clothes.

42 ₁go ¹into sth

to examine or discuss something carefully

Check
MEANING: a, c
GRAMMAR: a, b, c

Practise
1 a iii b v c i d ii e iv 2 a ...without going into what causes stress. b ...but I don't want to go into it. c ...but didn't go into how it started. d ...I'll go into what's involved. e ...but didn't go into details.

43 ｜go ＇through sth
to experience a difficult or unpleasant time or event

Check
MEANING: difficult, unpleasant
GRAMMAR: a, c

Practise
1 Suggested Answers: a ...he's just going through a difficult phase. b Everyone goes through a grieving process. c ...to imagine what he's gone through/what he's been going through. d We went through financial difficulties last year... e You've gone through a lot in recent years.

44 ｜go ＇through with sth
to do sth that you have planned or promised to do, even though it may be difficult or unpleasant

Check
MEANING: c
GRAMMAR: a, b, c

Practise
1 a go through with b went through with c go through with d going through with 2 It would be stupid not to do the interview: It would be stupid not to go through with the interview, I think. Well, we have finally decided to do it: Well, we have finally decided to go through with it...

45 ｜grow ＇out of sth
if a child **grows out of** clothes, he/she becomes too big to wear them; if you **grow out of** an illness, etc. it stops as you become older

Check
MEANING: 1 b 2 a
GRAMMAR: a, b

Practise
a Hay fever is an illness that people often grow out of as... b I used to bite my nails, but I've grown out of it now. c I've grown out of this skirt. d When did you grow out of asthma? e Analysts hope that the country will soon grow out of these problems/that these are problems the country will soon grow out of.

46 ｜keep ＇on; ｜keep ＇on doing sth
to continue without stopping NOTE This verb often shows that the speaker is angry about sb's behaviour. It can also be used in this way without 'on': Don't keep complaining!

Check
MEANING: continue, do not stop
GRAMMAR: a correct b Why does he keep on doing that? c He keeps on getting himself into trouble. d I kept on trying. NOTE This verb is not used in the progressive tenses.

Practise
1 a admiration b frustration c determination d support 2 Suggested Answers: a My neighbours keep on playing loud music at night! b My car keeps on

making a horrible noise. c Everyone keeps on spelling my name wrong.

47 ｜keep sb ＇on
to continue to employ sb, even though circumstances have changed

Check
MEANING: 1 a 2 b
GRAMMAR: b, d NOTE The pattern keep on workers is unusual.

Practise
1 a Most employees...are kept on until... b ...but they couldn't afford to keep him on... c I hope they'll keep me on for... d ...so they won't keep on everybody who starts working in July but... NOTE Very long objects usually come after the particle (on). 2 Suggested Answers: a In Britain, workers are kept on until they retire at 65. b You could be kept on part-time by your old company.
NOTE The verbs **take sb on** and **lay sb off** are in Really Learn 100 Phrasal Verbs for Business.

48 ｜let sb ＇off; ｜let sb ＇off sth
to allow sb not to do or pay sth

Check
MEANING: c
GRAMMAR: c He let her off it.

Practise
1 a iii b i c iv d ii 2 Suggested Answers: a I said I would let him off paying me back if... b I asked my manager if I could be let off the meeting. c If you're tired, I'll let you off coming with me.

49 ＇live on sth
to have a particular amount of money with which to buy everything you need

Check
MEANING: a
GRAMMAR: a, c

Practise
1 a income; to live on b live on; wages c pension; to live on 2 b, d

50 ｜look ＇into sth
to examine or consider sth carefully

Check
MEANING: c
GRAMMAR: a, b, e

Practise
1 a are looking into b look into it c look into d looked into e is looking into 2 Suggested Answers: Your letter could use the phrase 'I will look into your complaint...' or 'I will look into the matter...'

51 ｜look ＇out for sb/sth
to watch carefully for sb/sth

Check
MEANING: a true b true c false
GRAMMAR: a correct b I'll be looking out for you. c This is a book to look out for... d correct e I was looking out for that book, but...

Practise
a look out for b looking for c look out for d look out for e looked for

52 ˌmake sth ˈout

to be able to see, hear or understand sth, especially when it is difficult

Check

MEANING: **a**, **b**, **d**

GRAMMAR: **a**, **c**, **d** NOTE The pattern *make the shape out* is less common.

Practise

1 a made out **b** make out **c** make out **2** Suggested Answers: **a** I could just *make out* the door. **b** I can *make out* shapes but they're not very clear. **c** I can't *make him out* at all. **d** I can *make out* a few words.

53 ˌmake ˈup for sth; ˌmake ˈup for doing sth

to do sth to correct a bad situation

Check

MEANING: **a** good, bad **b** better

GRAMMAR: **b**, **c**, **d**, **f**

Practise

1 a made up for; ii **b** making up for; iii **c** make up for; i **2 a** ...to *make up for* overcharging me. **b** ...but it's got a lovely garden, which *makes up for* it.

54 ˌmess sb/sth ˈup; ˌmess ˈup

to spoil or ruin sb/sth; to do sth very badly

Check

MEANING: **a** true **b** false **c** false **d** true

GRAMMAR: **a** I've really messed it up this time. **d** He had been completely messed up by prison.

Practise

1 a I don't know how you could mess up... **b** ...it would be so easy to mess up. **c** ...or did you mess up? **2** Suggested Answers: Bob *messed up* breakfast and burnt the toast. He didn't see Mr Umar because his boss *had messed up*.

55 ˌmix sb/sth ˈup

to wrongly think that one person or thing is another person or thing

Check

MEANING: **c**

GRAMMAR: **a**, **b**, **c**, **e**

Practise

1 a mix us up **b** mix them up **c** mixed up **d** mixed her up with **2** Suggested Answers: I sometimes *mix up* the words 'lay' and 'lie'.

56 ˌmix sth ˈup

to change the order or arrangement of things in a confused or untidy way

Check

MEANING: **b**

GRAMMAR: **a** She's mixed up all the papers. **b** The letters were/have been mixed up. **c** She mixed them up. NOTE The pattern *mix the letters up* is less common. This verb is often used in the passive with *be* or *get*.

Practise

1 Suggested Answers: **a** ...but they have (all) been mixed up on the shelves. **b** They have been/were mixed up with the dirty ones. **c** ...he mixes them up. **d** Who (has) mixed them up? **e** ...and now all my notes have been/are mixed up.

57 ˌpass sth ˈon

to give sth to sb else

Check

MEANING: give

GRAMMAR: **a**, **b**, **d**, **e**

Practise

1 a is passed on **b** be passed on **c** been passed on **d** pass on **2** Suggested Answers: **a** Please *pass on* this leaflet to... **b** The gene for red hair *was passed on* from his father. **c** I got chickenpox and *passed it on* to...

58 ˌpick sth/sb ˈout

to choose or to recognize sth/sb from a number of people or things

Check

MEANING: **a**, **b**, **d**

GRAMMAR: **c**, **d**, **e** NOTE The pattern *pick a name out* is very rare.

Practise

1 a picking out, the best fruits to buy **b** pick...out, the freshest **c** pick...out, me **d** pick out, drivers who are going too fast **2 a** pick him out **b** to pick out **c** picked out **d** to pick out **e** picking out

59 ˌpick sth ˈup (1)

to learn a language, a skill, etc., or to get information, without making an effort

Check

MEANING: **c**

GRAMMAR: **a**, **b**

Practise

1 a iv **b** i **c** v **d** ii **e** iii **2** Suggested Answers: **a** You can *pick up* a lot of information... **b** I've *picked up* so many tips... **c** He *picks up* loads of facts... **d** Jana *picked up* Japanese... **e** Even experienced drivers *pick up* bad habits...

NOTE See also **pick up** in *Really Learn 100 Phrasal Verbs for Business*.

60 ˌpick sth ˈup (2)

to get or buy sth

Check

MEANING: **c**

GRAMMAR: **a**, **b**

Practise

1 a ...where she (had) picked it up. **b** I picked up €40... **c** ...we can't pick up the channel here. **d** I picked up the accent... **e** ...I couldn't pick up a signal. **f** Often people pick up the disease... **2 a** football **b** snooker **c** swimming

61 ˌpoint sb/sth ˈout

to show sb which person or thing you are referring to

Check

MEANING: **b**

GRAMMAR: **c** It was easy to see after she pointed it out.

Practise

1 a iii **b** i **c** iv **d** ii **2** Suggested Answers: **a** point it out **b** They pointed them out to you/they were pointed out to you... **c** ...he'll point her out (to you). **d** I'll point it out to you.

62 ˌpull sth ˈoff

to succeed in doing or achieving sth difficult, especially with the help of skill or luck

Check

MEANING: succeed in doing, difficult   NOTE This verb is often used to talk about winning in sport.
GRAMMAR: **b**, **d** NOTE The pattern *pull a win off* is very rare.

Practise

1 a pulling off **b** to pull it off **c** pull off **d** pulled off **e** to pull off **f** pulled it off **2** Suggested Answers: I *pulled off* a great win in my tennis match. I passed my exam! I can't believe I *pulled it off*!

63 ˌpull ˈthrough; ˌpull ˈthrough sth

to get better after an illness; to succeed in dealing with difficult problems

Check

MEANING: **b**, **c**
GRAMMAR: **a**, **b**, **e** NOTE The pattern *pull sb through (sth)* is also possible.

Practise

Suggested Answers: **a** The doctors do not know if he *will pull through*. **b** We're all praying that she *pulls through/will pull through*. **c** ...but they are beginning to *pull through* it/their ordeal. **d** ...to help it *pull through* the market downturn.

64 ˌput sth ˈback

to return sth to its usual place or to the place it was before

Check

MEANING: **a** where it was before **b** often **c** a thing
GRAMMAR: **a** correct **b** correct **c** Could you please put it back? **d** correct **e** I put it back immediately/I immediately put it back. **f** correct   NOTE The pattern *put back the book* is less common.

Practise

1 a put it back **b** take my books back **c** replace it **d** where you found it **2** Suggested Answers: **a** He never *puts* anything *back*. **b** ...you should *put* them *back* in their cases/boxes (after you've played them). **c** ...*put* it *back/put* your books *back*. **d** ...*put* the milk/butter *back*...

65 ˌput sb/yourself ˈdown

to criticize sb and make them feel stupid, especially in front of other people; to say sth that suggests that you have a low opinion of yourself

Check

MEANING: unkind, bad, are
GRAMMAR: **a**, **b**, **d**, **e**

Practise

1 a ii **b** v **c** iv **d** i **e** iii

66 ˈput sth down to sth

to consider that sth is caused by sth

Check

MEANING: explain, caused
GRAMMAR: **a**, **b**, **d**

Practise

1 a working **b** lying **c** playing **d** being **2** Suggested Answers: **a** Somebody looks unhealthy/is coughing, etc. **b** The fact that you didn't play well/do well in an interview, etc.

67 ˌput sb ˈout

to make trouble, problems, extra work, etc. for sb

Check

MEANING: **b**
GRAMMAR: **a**, **c** NOTE The pattern *put out my family* is very rare.

Practise

1 a no **b** yes **c** yes **d** yes **2 a** put you out **b** put you out **c** putting you out **d** doesn't put you out/isn't putting you out

68 ˌput sb ˈup

to let sb stay at your home; to arrange for sb to stay somewhere

Check

MEANING: **b**, **c**
GRAMMAR: **a**, **b**, **c**, **e**

Practise

1 Suggested Answers: **a** put him up **b** puts me up **c** were put up **d** putting somebody else up/putting up 3 other people, etc. **2** Suggested Answers: **a** My brother is *putting* me *up/will put* me *up*. **b** I know somebody who can/will *put* you *up*. **c** How will you *put* them all *up*? **d** They *were put up* in a school.
NOTE See also **put up sth** in *Really Learn 100 Phrasal Verbs for Business*.

69 reˈfer to sb/sth

to mention or speak about sb or sth

Check

MEANING: **a**
GRAMMAR: **a**, **c**, **d**

Practise

1 a iv **b** ii **c** i **d** v **e** iii **2** Suggested Answers: **a** ...but didn't *refer to* it again/never *referred to* it. **b** I'm not sure what/who you're *referring to*.

70 reˈmind sb of sb/sth

if sb/sth **reminds you of** sb/sth else in some way, they make you think about the other person, place, thing, etc. because they are similar

Check

MEANING: **a**
GRAMMAR: **c** She reminds me of my mother.   NOTE This verb is not used in the progressive tenses.

Practise

1 Suggested Answers: **a** She *reminds* me *of* a horrible teacher... **b** The town *reminded* me very much *of* Vevey... **c** That photograph always *reminds* me *of* our trip... **d** The smell...*reminded* me *of* my childhood.

71 ˌrun ˈinto sb

to meet sb by chance

Check

MEANING: **b**, **d**
GRAMMAR: **a**, **b**, **d**

Practise

1 a no **b** yes **c** no **d** no **e** yes **f** no **2 a** ...I would *run* into you here! **b** ...you *are* always running into... **c** Who did you say *you ran* into...

72 ˈsee to sb/sth

to deal with sth or help sb who needs you

Check
MEANING: c
GRAMMAR: b I'll see to it. e I'll see to it that she gets help.

Practise
1 a iii b i c v d ii e iv 2 Suggested Answers: I'll *see to* the flights/booking the flights. Could you *see to*...?

73 ˌset ˈout
to have a particular aim when you start to do sth

Check
MEANING: c
GRAMMAR: a, b

Practise
1 a ii b iv c i d iii 2 Suggested Answers: a It *sets out* to assess students' ability. b I *set out* to make a lot of money. c I *set out* to write a best-seller. d I *set out* to show that their results were wrong.

74 ˌset sth ˈout
to give all the details of sth in a clear and organized way

Check
MEANING: b
GRAMMAR: a, c, d, e NOTE The pattern *set plans out* is less frequent.

Practise
1 a setting out b are set out c sets out d set them out e set out f sets out 2 stating:...*setting out* clearly in writing why you would like this job.

75 ˌshow ˈoff
to do or say things to try and make people admire your possessions, abilities, etc.

Check
MEANING: 1 b 2 b
GRAMMAR: a, b, d

Practise
1 a about b to c to, about 2 a show off b showing off c showed off d showing off

76 ˌshow sth/sb ˈoff
to try to make people pay attention to sth/sb because you are proud of it/them

Check
MEANING: a
GRAMMAR: c ...showed her diamond ring off to her friends.

Practise
1 a ...show off new products. b ...showed off a new watch. c ...showing off her suntan. d ...show off his language skills. 2 Suggested Answers: I was very proud of my new MP3 player, and *showed* it *off* to all my friends.

77 ˌspread sth ˈout
to arrange a group of objects on a surface so you can see them all clearly

Check
MEANING: a arrange b on c away from d clearly
GRAMMAR: a, b, c, e NOTE The pattern *spread yourselves out* is used when people move away from each other.

Practise
1 a spread them out b spreading the various dishes out/spreading out the various dishes *or* and spread...

c spread their paintings out/spread out their paintings d spread out 2 Can you all *spread yourselves out* so...?

78 ˈstand for sth
to support sth; to be a symbol of sth

Check
MEANING: support, be a symbol of
GRAMMAR: a, b

Practise
1 a ...stands for greater integration between countries. b All organizations stand for protecting... c ...what the new president stands for.

79 ˌstand ˈout
to be much better or more important than other people or things

Check
MEANING: better, important, other
GRAMMAR: a, b, c NOTE This verb is often used with propositions such as *among, from, as* and *for*.

Practise
1 a for/because of b as c in d as/for e among/ above 2 Suggested Answers: a France really *stands out* as being the most beautiful country I have ever visited. b My brother really *stands out* in my family because he is the only one who doesn't wear glasses!

80 ˌstand ˈup for sb/sth/yourself
to support or defend sb/sth/yourself, especially when sb is criticizing them/it/you

Check
MEANING: a neither b b c b
GRAMMAR: b, d NOTE This verb is not used in the passive.

Practise
1 a, c, d 2 a I don't need you to stand up for me. b You have to learn to stand up for yourself. c Why didn't anyone stand up for me? d I stood up for him... e ...rather than standing up for him.

81 ˌstand ˈup to sb/sth
to resist sb/sth; to defend your position against a more powerful person or organization that is treating you badly or unfairly

Check
MEANING: more, badly, unfairly
GRAMMAR: a, c NOTE The passive is possible but almost never used.

Practise
1 c 2 Suggested Answers: a You have to *stand up to* him. b ...to see if they *will stand up to* her. c ...when you *stand up to* them.

82 ˈstick to sth
to continue doing or using sth, even if it is difficult

Check
MEANING: a, c
GRAMMAR: a, c NOTE This verb is almost never used in the passive.

Practise
1 a ii b iii c v d i e iv 2 a stick to b not sticking to
c to stick to d don't stick to e stuck to

83 ˌstick ˈup for sb/sth/yourself

to support or defend sb/sth

Check
MEANING: support, defend
GRAMMAR: a, c, d

Practise
1 a stick up for b sticks up for c stick up for d
sticking up for 2 a stuck up for b stick up for c stick
up for d sticks up for e sticking up for f stick up for
g stuck up for

84 ˌsum ˈup; ˌsum sth ˈup

to give the main details of sth in a short and clear way

Check
MEANING: b
GRAMMAR: a, b, d, e

Practise
1 a sum up b summed up c sum them up d summing
up 2 Suggested Answers: a To *sum up*,…know what
caused/the cause of the accident. b Let me *sum up* by
saying… c Well, he *summed up* by saying… d Well, to
sum (it) up,…is very bad.

85 ˌtake sth ˈback

to admit that what you said was wrong or that you should
not have said it

Check
MEANING: a
GRAMMAR: a, b, d, e NOTE The patterns *take my
comments back* and the passive are not very common.

Practise
1 I said he was unhelpful but I take it all back. 2
Suggested Answers: He had to *take back* the allegation.
It was a stupid comment and I *take it back*.

86 ˌtake sth ˈdown

to write sth down

Check
MEANING: c
GRAMMAR: a, b, c, e

Practise
1 a ii b iii c iv d i 2 Suggested Answers: a The police
officer *took down* my address/*took* my address *down* in
his notebook. b The reporters *were taking down* every
word she said. c …*taking down* the information Mike
was giving him.

87 ˌtake sb ˈin

to make sb believe sth that is not true

Check
MEANING: a
GRAMMAR: a He didn't take you in, did he? c He took me
in completely…

Practise
1 a take you in b taken in c takes/took me in d
taken in 2 a He took us in completely with… b
…stolen, taking us all in. c I was surprised at how easy
it was to take her in.

88 ˌtake sth ˈin

to understand or absorb sth that you hear, see or read

Check
MEANING: a true b false
GRAMMAR: a, c NOTE The pattern *take the situation in*
is less frequent and the passive is not used. The verb is
usually used in a negative way, with a word such as *not,
difficult,* etc.

Practise
1 a to take in b took in c taken it all in d be able to
take in 2 b …but I didn't really *take in* what she was
saying. c …and at first I didn't/couldn't *take in* what
had happened.

89 ˌtake sth ˈout; ˌtake sth ˈout of sth

to remove sth from somewhere; to carry sth with you
outside; to remove money from your bank account

Check
MEANING: b
GRAMMAR: b She took her keys out of her pocket.

Practise
a …so I took out the laptop/took the laptop out and
started… b Too many books are taken out of libraries,
and… c If you take out cash/take cash out with a credit
card… d …a metal box and take them out one at a time.

90 ˈtake to sb/sth

to start liking sb/sth

Check
MEANING: c
GRAMMAR: a, b NOTE The passive is not used.

Practise
1 a take to b taken to c take to d taking to e take to
2 Suggested Answers: a …never took to her teachers.
b Most of the team took to the new boss… c …but they
didn't take to each other at all.

91 ˌtear sth ˈup

to destroy paper, cloth, etc. by pulling it into several small
pieces

Check
MEANING: paper, plastic, cloth
GRAMMAR: a, b, c, e

Practise
1 tearing up; tear up; tear it up; torn up 2 Suggested
Answers: I would definitely *tear up* a photograph of
myself that I didn't like. I wouldn't *tear up* an important
document like a contract.

92 ˌthrow sb ˈout; ˌthrow sb ˈout of somewhere

to force sb to leave a place, their home, a job, etc.

Check
MEANING: c
GRAMMAR: a, c, f

Practise
1 b, c, d 2 Suggested Answers: b My brother's firm
threw him *out* because… c They *threw* me *out of* the
country because… d His wife *threw* him *out*.

93 ˌtry sth ˈon

to put on a piece of clothing to see if it fits and how it looks

Check

MEANING: c

GRAMMAR: b I love trying on clothes/trying clothes on.
d I love trying them on.

Practise

1 a a skirt/dress **b** trousers **c** a hat **d** shoes **e** a
coat/jacket **2 a** trying on **b** have tried on **c** trying on
d tried them on

94 ˌtry sth/sb ˈout

to test sth/sb to see how good and useful it/they are or how
suitable for a particular task or purpose before you decide
to use it/them

Check

MEANING: **a** no **b** no **c** yes

GRAMMAR: a, b, d, e

Practise

1 a ...try it out. **b** She tried out a few different jobs/
tried a few different jobs out before... **c** A new type of
hose was tried out/is being tried out by... **e** We decided
to try him out and... **2** Suggested Answers: **a** You
shouldn't be afraid to *try out* new things. **b** Why don't
we *try out* somewhere new/*try out* that new café?

95 ˌturn ˈinto sth; ˌturn sth ˈinto sth

to change and become sth else; to change sth so that it
becomes sth else

Check

MEANING: c

GRAMMAR: **d** They turned it into apartments.

Practise

1 a ii **b** i **c** v **d** iii **e** iv **2** Suggested Answers: **a** ...the
frog that turned into a prince? **b** ...they have turns into
a bitter row. **c** ...and turned into a parking lot.

96 ˌturn ˈout (1)

to take place or happen in the way mentioned; to develop or
end in a particular way

Check

MEANING: a

GRAMMAR: a, b

Practise

1 a iii **b** iv **c** ii **d** i **2** Suggested Answers: **a** How did
your first day *turn out*? **b** Don't worry. It*'ll turn out* OK.
c ...but it *turned out* much better than I'd hoped!
NOTE See also **turn sth out** in *Really Learn 100 Phrasal
Verbs for Business*.

97 ˌturn ˈout (2)

to be present at an event; to attend sth or to go somewhere

Check

MEANING: attend, go to

GRAMMAR: a, b

Practise

1 Suggested Answers: **a** 17 people turned out on
Thursday night. **b** Everybody turned out on Friday. **c**
15 people turned out on Saturday. **d** Nobody turned out
on Sunday. **2** Suggested Answers: **a** ...the whole town
turned out to say goodbye. **b** ...almost everyone *will
turn out* to vote. **c** ...everyone still *turns out* to watch.

98 ˌwalk ˈout; ˌwalk ˈout of sth

to leave a meeting, a performance, etc. suddenly before the
end, because you do not like it or are angry

Check

MEANING: leave, end, angry

GRAMMAR: a, d, e

Practise

1 b, d **2 a** walked out (of the room) **b** walk out (of the
classroom) **c** walking out/to walk out (of the cinema)
d walking out (of the office) **e** walked out of

99 ˌwalk ˈout; ˌwalk ˈout on sb/sth

to leave sb/sth you have a close relationship with or sb/sth
you are responsible for

Check

MEANING: c

GRAMMAR: a, c, d

Practise

1 a his wife **b** the children **c** her husband **d** her
colleagues/bosses **2 a** ...she has finally walked out.
b ...but she has a reputation for walking out on chat
show hosts. **c** ...I never thought he would just walk
out on me. **d** ...for walking out on his colleagues... **3**
Suggested Answers: **a** ...but he *walked out on* his country
and went... **b** That was the only job I've ever *walked out
on*. **c** ...I will never *walk out on* the band... **d** ...so she
walked out on her husband.

100 ˌwrap sth ˈup; ˌwrap sb/yourself ˈup

to cover sth in paper or other material, to protect it or
because you are giving it to sb as a present; to put warm
clothes, etc. on sb/yourself

Check

MEANING: **a** true **b** false

GRAMMAR: **d** She often forgets to wrap (herself) up in
warm clothes.

Practise

1 a iii **b** ii **c** iv **d** i **2 a** ...wrap up goods/wrap goods up
so securely? **b** ...*wrapped* up for winter! **c** ...*wrapping*
up gifts is... **d** ...*up* in hats and scarves...